WILL JAMES'
BOOK OF COWBOY STORIES

WILL JAMES'
BOOK OF

ILLUSTRATED BY WILL JAMES

COWBOY STORIES

NEW YORK

CHARLES SCRIBNER'S SONS

5-6-91

CONTENTS

WILL JAMES

ARIZONA—MORE THAN thirty years ago. The ol' Cross S
outfit was camped at Seven Mile. One of the boys
had gone into headquarters for chuck and he brought
back a *Sunset Magazine* he had found at the ranch, it seems
there was a drawing in the magazine he liked. There were
more than twenty riders around the fire that night, counting
reps and strays. As a waddie passed the magazine to me he
said, "Here's a feller that knows his riggin'."

As I remember, it was a drawing of a cow mired in a bog
hole, a wobbly calf stood beside her, in the background were
a couple of coyotes waiting to pull the calf down. The drawing was signed Will James III. I looked a long time. No
one except a cowboy could have made that drawing, and
there was a feel about it I liked.

Dave Reed spoke, "I worked with a Will James in Nevada
who was always drawing, he drew on every scrap of paper
he could find, even drew pictures on his tepee tent. Little
black-haired feller, good rider."

A few years later I was in New York—1926, I think—
and Lee Townsend brought Bill down to my boar's nest
where I was holed up for the winter. I'd seen many of Bill's
drawings in the meantime and admired his work very much.
When Lee introduced us I said, "Hell, you look more like

an Irish scholar than you do a cowpuncher." When Bill's eyes clouded I knew I'd hurt his feelings.

"I been hurt," he said, and he looked like a man who had been hurt. But when I told him what Dave Reed had said in camp that night at Seven Mile it pleased him, he remembered Dave. I told Bill how much I admired his drawings, liked some of the stories too. But I wondered if he was as good a cow hand as he claimed to be. He laughed, but he didn't commit himself. "People like 'em that way," he said. I mentioned certain artists who meant a lot to me: Daumier, Forain, Bellows. Bill had never heard of them, so we talked horses that night.

Then I was with Bill at the Rodeo in Chicago as guest of the Chicago Rodeo Association three successive years, and we saw a lot of each other. Bill was doing a short piece and a drawing each day for one of the Chicago papers, and that ol' fountain pen of his did double duty. He wrote the piece first and always gave it to me to read. He wrote in a peculiar script. There were no corrections and he wrote exactly as he talked, but watching him make the drawings was what fascinated me.

Most artists I have known sweat out their drawings, but Bill always seemed to have the picture as a whole in his mind. And there were no false starts, no fumbling. He'd make a line or two at the top of the page, a few at the bottom. 1 couldn't make head or tails as I watched, until suddenly a horse came to life and exploded right off the paper.

As the cowboys say, Bill was always "muyo coyote." He would seldom commit himself, and yet he told me of his trouble in Nevada. Later he told about it in LONE COW-BOY, and the first part of that book I think is one of the finest things Bill ever wrote. And there was a short piece that will always stay in my mind—when Bill was starting out on an all-night ride south a three-legged coyote followed a piece, the coyote had been in a trap. Like Bill he had been hurt, too.

I saw him only occasionally after Chicago but we kept in touch with each other as long as Bill lived. There was always a little picture on his letters. There's one before me now— fall of the year, when the hair gets long on a pony. He left us all too soon. His was a great talent. Somehow one always remembers the best things a man has done. His drawings are already collectors' items. And as long as anyone cares for cow country his stories will be read, for Bill knew his riggin'.

Ross Santee

FIRST STORY

ON THE DRIFT

I T MUST BE great to be a cowboy, so free and have nothing to do but ride and ride and ride."

That's what a feller says to me one time. I didn't answer him, just sort of grinned at him and says "You bet." . . . There'd been only one way of answering him, not with words, but with a chance for him to try and be a cowboy for a year or so . . . and then I'd like to heard what he'd have to say.

Of course he might of fooled me and liked it, but I'm thinking that his ideas of the life would of changed a heap.

Like for instance. . . .

We was gathering big beef steers one fall. That was up in the northern prairies and where you could ride thirty miles in any direction without striking a break or hollow that was any deeper than a buffalo wallow. The weather had been acting mighty queer, and as the old timers said, queerer than they'd ever seen it. One morning would be fine and clear and warm, too warm, by noon there'd be a wind spring up and bring on thunder showers, and by sundown we'd be digging up all the clothes we owned and putting 'em on to break the cold wind. By the time night come and when we all had to take turns about on guard there'd be a regular blizzard howling, stinging snow would be hitting our faces and making the beef herd hump up. You'd swear it was middle winter.

We'd be up at four o'clock the next morning. It'd still be snowing and the wind blowing cold, with a dark gray sky hanging over us like a blanket from the North Pole. We'd put on frozen socks inside of wet boots, most all our clothes would be froze and stiff, so was our saddles and ropes, and every horse in the remuda had a kink in their back, was full of snorts and frisky to handle. The most of 'em bucked, many that hadn't bucked for a long time, and even the gentlest ones was hard to get near after they was caught. The sudden cold sure made 'em mean.

We'd have our coffee and line out to riding before daylight, on a white landscape and facing cold winds under gray skies. By middle forenoon it would stop snowing and then there'd be a break up above, after a while the sun would be showing thru, the clouds would clear away and by noon we'd be back to camp with the morning's roundup and go to shedding most of the clothes we had on. Then it'd turn hot, after a while another wind from another direction would spring up and bring on more thunder showers. Thunder and lightning while there was snow on the ground. And that night it'd be snowing and cold again.

That freak weather lasted for about three days. During that time the roundup wagon had to make camp on the open prairie, many miles from any shelter and wood, and what wood was brought along in an extra wagon was fast dwindling away. The cook was the only one that was allowed to use any of it, no separate fires for us cowboys, we had to use the cook's fire when we could and the twenty of us had a hard time getting a place near it whenever we come into camp.

Our roundup outfit moved camp every day, it took six big horses to pull the chuck wagon acrost the soaked prairie, four to pull the wagon that was loaded with our bed rolls, and four more to pull the wood and water wagon. The tracks of the wagons cut down six inches into the tough sod, and in some places the wheels sunk to the hubs. The country was sure wet, everything was wet, our boots and spurs was all slippery mud, our stirrups was slippery, and so was our horses, slippery to ride.

It would be a few days yet before we'd get thru combing the big prairie for the beef steers that was wanted for the fall shipment, and in that time we'd have to camp where the world was level as a floor, with no extra wood or shelter and where whatever the heavens handed out could sure reach us.

The moisture was fine for the stock, every buffalo wallow was full of water, where water hadn't been the whole summer before and now they was having a chance to get at the tall grass that hadn't been touched during the whole time.

The loose stock was doing fine, and so was the two thousand steers we'd gathered, but with the steers they was getting hard to hold at night, maybe it was from the change of heat during the day to sudden cold and snow during the night. We sure felt that change ourselves and agreed pretty well with the steers that a stampede wouldn't go bad. It'd sort of warm a feller up.

It was on the third night of the stormy weather that the steers did break into a dandy stampede, and even after the wagonboss put four men on each shift and warning us to be sure and hold them steers. I don't think any of us tried to hold 'em any too much, we was cold.

I happened to be on shift when the stampede started, it

was during the "grave-yard" shift (from midnight till two), lightning had been playing longer that night, some of it played mighty close to the herd and when one bolt landed to within fifty feet of it and split a big boulder the whole herd just picked itself up like it was one steer and lit out. It wasn't but a minute afterwards when a regular cloudburst hit us, a feller couldn't see six inches ahead, my horse's feet sunk ankle deep in the sod and in some little swales he'd slip and slide. But he was a good horse and stayed on his feet.

The lightning and rain kept a pattering around us, the herd was running good, but I noticed by the flashes of lightning that it was splitting. I tried to crowd the bunch I had with the main bunch, but in the dark my horse was just another steer and was crowded out of the way and my holler couldn't be heard on account of the noise and splashing. When I got to feeling a few horns alongside of my leg every time I tried to bend my bunch I soon realized that I'd just as well try to turn a locomotive off the track as to try and bend them steers. They couldn't see nor hear me and they was wanting to run.

I tried to bend the leaders time and time again, and kept on trying. I'd hit the closest ones over the head with my coiled rope, but that didn't faze 'em. I emptied my six-shooter in front of their noses, and that checked 'em no longer than the time it took for the flash and report of my shots to die out, then they'd come right on again.

The steers kept on running even after the lightning died down. They was warmed up now, all excited and het up on the subject, and I knowed they'd be hard to stop till they tired out pretty well. That might be five or maybe ten miles from where they'd started.

I kept on doing my best to turn the leaders. We struck

prairie dog towns a couple of times and as some steers would stick a leg in a hole and turn over that would check the herd some, but not enough so they wouldn't pick up speed again soon as them towns was crossed, and as the last lightning flashes dimmed away and I tried to locate the main herd by 'em I seen that I was by myself and with a little bunch that'd split loose from it. There wasn't a sign of the main herd or any part of it to be seen nowheres.

I sure missed that lightning because the night was dark as a stack of black cats. The rain kept a pouring, and then a sudden strong wind came up and was so fast that even at the speed I was riding I felt it pushing my horse along. The steers went right with it for a spell, then finally begin to slow down. I had 'em then, and in a few minutes more I got 'em stopped. Stopped, but not turned because none of 'em could be made to face the heavy rain that the wind pounded onto 'em.

I figured I was about seven or eight miles from camp when I got the steers stopped. I knowed I couldn't drive 'em back till the wind and rain let up, for as it was I'd be doing mighty well if I just kept 'em from drifting on. So, there was no chance of being relieved off my shift on guard that night, and I settled down to staying with the cattle and keep 'em from drifting as much as I could.

The heavy rain poured on then it begin to get cold, mighty cold, and I didn't believe it was possible but the wind got stronger, after a while I begin to feel snow on my face and it wasn't long when there wasn't no more rain, it was all snow, real honest-to-god snow, and backed by a real honest-to-god wind. It was one of these blizzards that you sometimes hear about and makes you shiver even while standing by a red hot stove.

To say I was comfortable would sure be a beautiful lie. My slicker was in camp, where most slickers are when you need 'em the most, I had a heavy duck coat on but the rain had went thru that and soon as the cold and snow come it froze stiff. My legs was the only part of me that was dry, they was covered with a good pair of shaps'.

With the blizzard a howling the little herd I had begin to drift. There was no use trying to stop and hold 'em, I'd only wore my horse out and while I'd be riding in front of one part of the herd the other part would keep on drifting anyhow, so I let 'em drift and checked 'em as much as I could by doing as little riding as possible.

I rode in the lead of the herd the rest of the night, and when daylight come and I seen no sign of the blizzard breaking up I didn't try to check the herd no more. It looked now like the storm would be sure to last at least all that day, and knowing that even if some riders did find me and helped that the herd couldn't be turned to face the blizzard I let 'em drift to their hearts' content. They wanted shelter and so did I, and all I done while I shivered and my teeth chattered was to ride around the herd and see that it kept together. It was hard to see them all in the whirling snow but I made a rough count of about a hundred and fifty head, a plenty big enough herd so that no cowboy would leave and let scatter.

I wished now there hadn't been no stampede and that we'd all worked harder to stop it. If it hadn't been for that I'd been in camp now, in the shelter of canvas and drinking hot coffee. As it was it looked like I'd be missing that coffee for sometime to come. I didn't expect any riders out looking for me, if any was it wasn't at all likely they'd find me because in the thick snow a feller couldn't see much further than the length of his horse, and if any riders did find me they couldn't do any more than what I was doing alone, they'd just have to drift too.

I figured that, if I had my directions right, I'd be hitting a creek that I knowed of within fifteen or twenty miles from where I was. The creek cut deep in the prairie had steep

breaks on both sides and thick clumps of willows along the banks. There's where there'd be shelter and where the herd would be glad to stop and easy to hold, I could build a fire too as there was plenty of dead wood all along the creek.

The thought of a fire made me do better than to just let the herd drift, I went to driving 'em and making 'em go faster, away from camp and towards that shelter. For the way the weather behaved it looked like it was due to be the same for another day or so, and being I couldn't get back to camp with the herd I hit for shelter, and where I could build a fire.

I went with the wind, kept the herd at a good walk and the steers being all big and strong I made pretty good time. The day wore on that way, the blizzard still a howling right along and in some places the snow had drifted pretty deep. The running, then the drifting and the cold begin to show on the steers, they'd shrunk quite a bit, but being it was early fall with some more warm weather to be expected a few days of good grazing would put 'em back to where they was.

I drove 'em on, expecting any time now to see the leaders drop over the breaks into the creek bottom. I couldn't see the leaders, but it wouldn't be long after they hit the creek when I'd know.

But the creek must of been further than I figured. It was beginning to get dark and I still hadn't got to it, when, as I thought, I should of got to it by the middle of the afternoon. Then I got to wondering, wondering if the wind hadn't switched some and made me loose my direction. As night came on I knowed daggone well that's what had happened, but I didn't think I was far from the creek. I tried to turn the leaders to sidling against the storm, but I had to give that up because none of the leaders nor any in the herd would sidle against the stinging snow and cold wind.

There was nothing for me to do except to let 'em drift with the storm. I knowed for sure by then that we'd missed the creek and I wasn't driving the cattle no more, I just kept 'em together and let 'em drift and settled down to "nothing to do but ride and ride and ride."

Only, sometimes I walked, I had to or I'd of froze stiff. My horse was pretty tired too, and ganted up as much as I was.

It was sure a long night, and I was mighty sleepy, but I didn't dare sleep for fear I'd freeze to death, sleep is the first step to that the rest comes easy. I'd walk till I was tired out then I'd ride till I was about froze and then I'd walk some more. I kept that up all night and drifted on with the herd till finally the sky begin to light up and another day come.

It might be wondered at why I didn't quit the herd and hit back for camp or shelter. There's only one answer to that, it's against cowboy religion and a *cowboy* never quits a herd.

But another day of that blizzard and I would of had to quit the herd, or else my carcass would of been preserved in a snow bank and not been found till the snows melted, maybe away into the following spring. But as good luck would have it, mighty good luck, it wasn't long after daylight come when it quit snowing, the wind had went down a consider-

able too and now I could see a long ways.

The first thing I noticed was the breaks of the creek I'd been trying to get the cattle to. It was only a couple of miles away and we'd been drifting right along it, most likely all night.

But now the cattle could be drove back to the main herd at camp, and I sure drove 'em because I figured I had about twenty-five miles to go to get there and I was mighty hungry and sleepy. I was sure glad when a little before noon I seen three riders coming my way, they was from the roundup wagon and out looking for me and my herd, they took charge of the herd and told me to hit for camp. I done that, but before I started I relieved one of the boys from his sack of tobacco, I hadn't had a smoke since early the day before and that was as bad as going without something to eat.

It was while I was rolling a smoke that the boys told me the roundup wagon was moving ten miles down country to meet the herd. The main herd and all had been on the drift. Well, that was ten miles less for me to ride and that sure didn't make me mad.

When I found the wagon, the pilot and a few other cowboys was setting up camp, the cook already had the fire going and the coffee was near boiling. I camped right by the fire and that big black pot, drinking cup after cup of the black coffee, and as I begin to warm up some and feeling a little more awake, I got to hearing from the other boys around that I wasn't the only one that had drifted with a split of the herd. For after the stampede had started all hands had got on their night horses to help stop it but they hadn't got there in time to help us who'd been separated each with our little herds. Two other riders had each been left by their lonesome the same as I had.

SECOND STORY

THE BEST RIDING
AND ROPING

A COLD NOVEMBER WIND was blowing as a cowboy rode down the point of a low ridge to where little of that sharp wind could reach him. There he stopped, got off his horse, shouldered against him like as to keep warmth with him, and with numbed fingers went to rolling a smoke.

His eyes wasn't on his cigarette as he rolled it, they was as had been for many days on a big herd of grazing cattle which he was at the edge of and most always steady watching that none strayed away.

He wasn't the only cowboy doing the same, there was six altogether at different points bordering that herd, and all was well needed, for that herd numbered over ten thousand head. Ten thousand head of mostly long-horn stuff, the rest of mixed, with a showing of the new imported Hereford, all steers, none less than four years old and from there on up to an unguessable age, but all fat as butter after ranging on the grassy northern plains. And they was now ready for shipment.

There'd been a few days of slow trailing to the shipping point, and to allow the cattle to fill and rest up well so as to have all the weight possible on 'em before loading 'em into the cars. For the long steel trail to market one extra day was allowed. The cars had been ordered, five trains of 'em and two engines to each, and now the big herd was being "loose herded" (scattering) and held ready to within a few miles of the shipping yards, just far enough so the cowboys with the herd could see the water tank by the railroad and hanker to have the shipping over with so they could have their well-deserved fun in the little cow town afterwards. A little of that goes well with any red-blooded human that's seen plenty of hard riding and long hours in the saddle, in all kinds of weather, day and night and from six to nine straight months.

That's a worrying time for the cow boss, to keep all of his cowboys with the herd until the stock is loaded in the cars and shipping is done, for then's when all hands are needed, more so than with the every-day work on the range. It's ticklish work to get the spooky stock in the shipping yards, and one little stampede might mean much loss on the weight of the cattle.

This cowboy at the point of the low ridge and about half froze wasn't worried much about cattle per weight. He was wishing they was all loaded in the cars and on their way, for outside of one day in middle summer, when he bowed his neck and told the wagon boss (cow foreman) that he was going to town wether he liked it or not, he'd been out on the range for eight straight months and sleeping on the ground for six of them months. That was when he could find time to sleep, which was about six hours out of the twenty-four.

So, he was kind of entitled to at least a good plate of ham and eggs for a change, a bath, a change to new clothes, a hair cut on head and face, and then a saunter on for a little fun along with the other boys. Then's when the little old cow town would come to life, and it'd always prepare for it.

But after a few days the fun would wear out, along with his money, and he'd hit for the range again, to some winter cow camp getting snowbound cattle thru drifts and where he'd be good until spring come and roundup started again.

After long months of hard riding the cowboy is anxious to have the shipping over with and work done for a spell, but after a long winter of snow bucking he's just as anxious to be on roundup again and out of permanent camps.

This cowboy, Flint Spears by name, wasn't thinking of winter camps or roundups as he smoked his cigarette and seen that his part of the herd didn't graze too far out. He was thinking of some ways and means to make his long summer's wages last longer and do better for him than all the times he hit town before. He was thinking on that platter of ham and eggs in a warm restaurant as the first thing he'd get, when glancing away beyond over the earth he seen a long dark ribbon, much darker than the brown earth and about two miles long. It was cattle, another herd, and looked like about the same size as the one he was with. It was just coming in, to ship too.

"Well," thought Flint, "Old Sol Burney and the cow boss of what ever that other herd is should of got together as to their shipping dates,—a bad night, a little stampede and big herds like these so close together would soon mix. It'd sure take plenty of time and work to cut out and get each herd straight again, not counting the poundage that'd be lost in the rounding up and cutting out and the expense of keep-

ing the trains waiting. Jumping Jehosphat! that'd sure be
some mixup and gathering." He grinned at the thought.
"But let 'er go Gallagher."

He watched and then seen that the long herd begin to
point away. "That's better," Flint remarked, and by the time
it was held it was a good five miles of prairie distance away.

The days being short there was three short "dayherd"
shifts, but the night guard shifts made up for that, for the
eighteen riders, taking turns of six at a time, stood three
hours at each shift, making nine hours of night guard and
the remaining hours again split in three shifts for dayherd.

Counting the cow boss, the cook and flunky, horse wrangler
and nighthawk, there was twenty-three men with the Seven
H. L. 7L herd, an above-average bunch of men of all parts
of the cow country, from Mexico to Canada, and Old Sol
Burney always prided himself, and boasted when he could,
that there wasn't another outfit between the two borders or
acrost the both of 'em that had a crew that could begin to
compete with his in roping, riding, or handling a herd. He
treated his men according and they treated him the same,
and even tho his boast had never been called there always
comes a time, like with any boast.

Flint had been on the afternoon shift, and when him and
the five other riders was relieved by another set of six and
rode into camp for supper there was a visitor, the cow boss
of the herd that'd just been trailed in and of an outfit two
hundred miles the opposite direction of the 7L, it was the
"Three T" 𝔜 outfit. They was doing extra heavy shipping
that fall, even to fair "she-stuff," and there was around
twelve thousand head in their herd, with a crew of twenty-
one men.

There was visiting between the two camps that evening,

and cowboys who hadn't seen one another, some of 'em for many years, met again and talked over old times.

But as wonders never cease and as good or bad always seem to come in threes, there was a third herd spotted the next afternoon, as big a herd as the 7L or the ✡ and "Doggone it," thought Flint, "where was all the stock cars going to come from to handle all this shipping? There'd be a couple of herds due to do some holding, but he hoped it wouldn't be the 7L because this dayherding sure wasn't to his liking."

But Flint didn't have to fret about that third herd because it was a stock herd (cows, weaners, yearlings, etc.) from the Slash A —A outfit and only being shifted to another range further on south to winter.

And that evening while the herds was being held five miles or more apart, representing over thirty thousand cattle altogether, sixty cowboys and four hundred saddle horses was a congregation of bellering, nickering and talking that sure enough went to make it cow country.

All but about twenty men on shift with the herds and "remudas" (saddle-horse bunches) gathered at the 7L camp that evening. A beef had been killed and the three cooks and flunkies pitched in to cooking the supper. A separate big fire was built, for the evening was plenty chilly, and there all gathered around it is where serious visiting talk begin and went on. It got less serious as it went on and more on the joking side. Then a couple of precious mouth organs and mouth harps was dug up and good attempts was made at good old tunes, such as, "That fateful night she wore a rose of white," and the likes.

The older men didn't pitch in with the singing much, they'd listen once in a while but they was more for talking "cow." The most of 'em talked cow all thru the good supper that was spread out in the Dutch ovens, skillets and pots that was by the cooks' fire, and naturally, when you talk cow the cowhorse is brought in, and roping and riding in general.

And naturally, too, that brings on telling of happenings to show how good each man's horse is, or how tough and bad. All depends wether they're cowhorses or outlaws, one is mighty good and the other is mighty bad, either better or worse than the other feller's. There wasn't so much bragging for each man's own roping or riding ability, but one could brag about the other on that, and that was well done.

So well done that as each of the three cow bosses begin bragging about their own riders, is when Old Sol reared up to boast again and made the first offer to bet a hundred dollars that he had the best riders and ropers of the three outfits.

At that statement all the boys quieted sudden. It was a big statement for anybody to make and some call to it was expected. And this time Old Sol didn't get away with his boast, for the ⋎ cow boss called his bet and raised it to two hundred. Old Sol grinned and grabbed at the chance.

"But we'll do it this way," says the ⋎ cow boss. "We'll lay a hundred on the bucking horse riding and a hundred on the steer roping, in two separate bets, and that way" he grinned, "you *might* make it to win."

Old Sol snorted and agreed. And now something was expected for the —A cow boss. He didn't seem so very anxious. He thought a while and finally said:

"I'll tell you what I'll do. I'll bet one hundred and fifty, and knowing you won't want to use your beeves for roping I'll furnish the stock for that purpose for the other fifty. I've got some plenty wiry steers, not fat enough to ship but'll sure make fine roping."

That was a decided go and all three shook hands on it. Now, when would the doings be coming off? And that was decided by the cow boss of the stock herd.

"Well," he says, "I've got to move on with my herd and I can't lay over one day. Can't we make it tomorrow?"

They could, and as they went to deliberating about this and that they got to thinking, how about the judges? None of the cow bosses nor any of the cowboys would do because they'd naturally be for their own outfit. It would have to be some neutral judges, judges who wouldn't be favoring any of the outfits.

"I'll tell you what I'll do," Old Sol says sudden. "I have to go to town early in the morning to see about the cars I ordered anyway, and I'll look for somebody there."

"Yes, good idea," says the 𝔶 man, "and we'll go with you too because we'll want some say about the picking of them judges."

Old Sol grinned. "All right," he says, at the same time gave the two a nudging look. Then the three walked away from the fire a piece and in low tones begin to confab.

When they got back the cowboys expected some kind of an announcement, and there was. Old Sol looked at all of 'em around the fire, and then he spoke.

"You all heard us doing the betting," he begins, "and now each one of us need the best riders and ropers to back us up. Any of you boys want to come in on this let us know in the morning. Tell the boys that's on shift now the same thing when you boys on the next shift go to relieve 'em.

"Each outfit can only use three for the broncho busting (there was no such term as bronc riding then) and the same for roping steers. There'll be two prizes for each of the doings, fifty dollars for the best and twenty-five for the second best. That's all, boys."

"No, that ain't all," says the ⵝ cow boss, coming to the front. "We don't want any of you boys loping into town tonight when off guard. Not till after the shipping is done, boys, and then you can put 'er on as wild as you want to, and maybe have another riding and roping doings. Now that is all."

Some of the boys grinned under their hat brims at one another at that, but the cow bosses wasn't much afraid of them going to celebrating until the work was done. One or two might go to hankering too strong and being so close to town might weaken, but that happens in all walks of life and with folks that never knew what it is to be away from towns for over a week at a time once a year. The difference is that, during them days, the cowboy might see town for a week only once or twice a year.

Soon as the dayherd shift went on the next morning and the herds was quietly grazing from their "bed grounds" (where the cattle is held to bed down during the night) to different creeks for water the three cow bosses saddled up and headed for the little cow town ten miles away. The first place they headed for when they got there was the freight depot, and then Old Sol found out that his cars wouldn't be there till that afternoon. At any other time he'd of got sort of peeved but this time it was all right, and loading could be done until the first train was loaded even if it took until away into the night. It's no harder to load at night than in daytime.

That attended to, they rode on the livery stable and told the stable man of what they was looking for and what for. To that the stableman's eye brightened a bit and he says:

"Well I've only rode for about forty years before I got

this barn, and I might be some kind of a judge."

He mentioned some of the outfits he rode for and before the long herds begin to be trailed north and that sure qualified him for one judge, but there'd need to be one more and Sol asked the old cowboy stableman where they'd be likely to find that other one.

The stableman didn't hesitate none in thinking of another. "There's the sheriff," he says. "There was a time when he sure used to could stomp 'em, and he could throw a mean loop too. You'll find him either at his office this time of morning or at *Bill's Place*."

Being that *Bill's Place* was the first along the one main street to the sheriff's office, the three stopped there, and there they found the sheriff taking his "morning's morning." His eyes also brightened up some when he was told what was wanted of him. He deputized the bartender right there and then to take charge and he was ready to go.

"There might be a few boys amongst all that bunch that I might want as guests for the State anyhow," he says, "and I'd like to look 'em over."

"If that's the kind of a judge you're going to be," comes back the ⅄ man, "you better stay where you are. You can do your State work after we're thru with these herds."

"Well," grins the sheriff, "I can at least look at 'em, can't I?"

After some little understanding talk they hit for the stable. The stableman had his own and the sheriff's horse saddled when they got there and all headed for the ⅂ wagon. Every cowboy not on shift from the three wagons, over forty of 'em, was waiting there when they rode up, and in the rope corral, instead of the regular ⅂ remuda, was the "rough string" (spoiled outlaw horses) of the three outfits, about forty head of the worst horses in the country to pick from for the bucking horse riding.

The horses that had been kept up and rode in was most all dayherd horses, the few gentle ones in a cowboy's string. They'd be used for "snubbing" the outlaws while being saddled. Then some of the boys that was to rope had saddled the tops of the top horses of each remuda for that purpose. All was well mounted and ready, and now the names of the men that wanted to ride and rope for the prizes had been put on three pieces of paper, one for each outfit, and handed to the cow bosses to peruse.

About all of the cowboys excepting the too old a ones had put their names down on the list, for bucking horse riding or roping, and some for both of the doings. The three bosses had to grin with pride at all the names on their lists.

"Well," the sheriff remarked, as he looked over their shoulders at 'em, "it looks like you're all pretty well full handed."

"Yes," Sol snorts back at him, "and don't you be picking any names off these lists either, not till after shipping anyhow."

As had been made understood to the cowboys the night before, only six was to be picked out for the two doings (termed event, now days). That was three for bucking horse riding and three for roping from each outfit, and now the three bosses, knowing their men as they did, went to checking on their lists the ones that'd be most apt to do the winning for 'em, their top hands in riding and roping.

There was a few on the list wanted that was on shift and them was sent for and replaced by some whose names wasn't on the list. But a couple of them was wanted for other things, and when they heard that the sheriff was to be one of the judges they sent word back that they'd changed their minds. Others was then put in their places, and when the selection was made and come time for the names to be called there was a hesitation amongst the bosses as to which one was to be the first to do the calling. Then them bosses noticed too that there was worried looks and fidgety actions amongst the cowboys for fearing they'd be left out. That'd be mighty humiliating, for any cowboy that can ride and rope halfways well thinks he's as good as any, his pride is mighty sensitive as to that, and one being chosen and another near as good being left out is a ticklish thing to do, especially with a cow outfit and at shipping time, for the ones left out might get up on their high horses, tell their bosses to go to the hot place and hit for town where there's no telling what they might do if they got on a rampage. As has been in some cases, the police force couldn't compete and neither could the soldiers that was called from the nearest forts, for the boys had to have their fun or their fights whichever way they felt, and it was found out they was best to be left alone, for seldom was there any trouble hunters among 'em.

Thinking all of that over from experience, the three bosses went into another private confab, and when it was over, Old Sol delivered the decision again.

"Well, boys," he begins, "we decided we couldn't pick any six best men out of each outfit. We figured you all to be the best and all rope and ride that wants to. The prizes still stand the same, two for riding and two for roping. Do your best, boys, and may the best men win."

There was no "Wild West, Whoopees!" as that was listened to and taken in, but the show of the sudden vanishing tenseness replaced by broad grins, near like that of a man who's given a chance for his life after being condemned to

death, more than made up for any show holler that ever
was invented.

The only ones that felt sorry for themselves now was the
boys on shift. They'd have to hold their herds to grazing
as usual and a good distance away, with not even a chance
for a far-away look. But the cooks and flunkies was all on
the job at the 7L wagon where the bucking horse riding was
going to take place. The "nighthawks" (night horse herder
and wrangler) who should of been catching up on their sleep
had no thought for that and was on hand too. Even the day
horse wranglers took chances of being bawled out by their
bosses, left their remudas on good grass where they figured
they'd stay and rode in, hoping not to be noticed, to watch
the doings. For that was a day of a lifetime, and no contest,
duel, bull fight, game or demonstration could of got any one
up on their toes as that range gathering of riders got themselves up in their stirrups. For most all would be riding
against one another, and it wasn't only one outfit against the
other but rider against rider even with the same outfit, for
only the best man won, regardless, and the prize wouldn't
be considered with the pride in winning. No gladiator ever
entered an arena, and no boxer or wrestler ever crawled thru
the ropes with more at stake to their hearts than each one
of these cowboys had. It wasn't going to be no knitting doings, only maybe bones afterwards.

There was no town folks gathered to see the doings, only
the sheriff and the stableman, and they couldn't exactly be
called that, for both had sat many a horse for many a year
and their "rigs" (saddles) wasn't hung up yet. There was
no grandstand only the prairie sod and a horse under each
spectator, or the chuck wagon for the cooks and flunkies.

The saddles was most all slick, narrow forked double

rigs, loose hackamore on the horse's head, and there was no rules only to sit up and ride. There was no use of mentioning that a rider was scratched out the second he touched the saddle horn or any part of the saddle with either hand. That was the same as being throwed.

Old Sol, being he'd been the leader in saying the first word, gave the word to start in by saying, "All right, boys. I'll call your names as they are on the 7L list. Crockett (the 𝔶 boss) and Davis (—A boss) will call their own list for their own riders, and when I call each one of you boys that's with my wagon (outfit) why, doggone you all, *ride,* ride like you know how. You'll be riding for yourselves and the 7L."

At a sign from Old Sol a cowboy rode up, and from the outside of the cable corral dabbed his rope over the head of a smooth-built 7L bay and led him out a-fighting thru a long span of the single cable which was the gate and let down to the ground by a wrangler to let the horse step over and out.

As the bay was led out snorting at the end of the rope, Old Sol called the first name on his list, and another cowboy of his, rope in hand, slid off his horse, picked up the bay's front feet with his ready loop, and the bay stood stock still. He was a wise outlaw, like most all of 'em are in the "rough string." And he knew better than fight the foot rope for he'd run against it many times before, only to a hard fall. That same cowboy then walked up to him and slipped a hackamore over his head, blindfolded him with a gunnysack and handed the hackamore rope to the man who first roped him to now do the snubbing.

The bay's head snubbed close to the saddle horn, the cowboy took his saddle off the horse he'd been on and, without blanket, slipped it on the bay's quivering back, cinched it well, and watching his eye for a hoof, slid into the saddle without the horse hardly knowing it. The hackamore rope from the snubber's saddle horn was handed the rider while he "felt" of his saddle, and then the blind was pulled off without the bay hardly knowing he'd been saddled and that there was a rider on him.

But that bay cocked one ear and he didn't waste no time blinking at the early-day sun; his head felt free and that's all he needed. He didn't give the rider a chance to get set with a few straight ahead jumps; instead he stuck his nose in the ground from the start, and pivoted there and seeming like begrudging tearing up too much country, stuck in one spot about twice his length, but what little land he took he sure made use of and gave his rider no lead as to wether

he was going to fall back, turn over, go thru the earth as
he landed or scrape a bird's wing as he went up. He was no
spinner, just a good crooked hard-hitting horse that made
his rider ride.

The rider rode and he knew he had before he got thru.
It was a case of a good rider on a good bucking horse.

$$* \quad * \quad * \quad * \quad *$$

Name after name was called, tough horses was roped,
snubbed, saddled and rode or rode at, and all the while
there was one cowboy getting nervous, for as the names was
called he seen where his had been skipped. His, when he
wrote it down was about the fourth on the list, and when
the eighth rider came out and still no call for him he figured
something was wrong.

Good tough horses came out, good rides was made on the
old slick trees, a couple of riders got throwed and the judges
was busy marking down one, two, three, erasing, and as another rider would come out they would maybe erase three
by one name and put down two or four, all depended how
the rider averaged up with the others.

The ninth horse was roped and made the whale line sing
as he was led out. He was a rangy blue roan with a head the
size, and about the shape, of a full-grown anvil, looked
like about the same weight, too, and when that horse was
brought to a fighting standstill for breath is when Old Sol
figured the judges needed a breathing spell too. It was during that time that he done a little impressive announcing,
to the judges, but also for all present.

"Now, Judges," he begins, "cool your heads a bit, because even tho you've already seen some mighty good riding on some good ponies ("pony" doesn't mean a pony—the

horse might easy weigh twelve hundred), here's another that'll gives you a chance at your ability as to judging good bucking horseflesh and a good rider astraddling it when you see it. Watch close."

Old Sol paused for a minute to let that announcement sink in then he called. "Flint Spears," he says, "this is your horse."

Flint's heart was good or he'd of dropped dead as his name was called following such an announcement, specially after thinking he'd been skipped. As it was it lost a couple of beats as he slid off his horse to claim the rangy blue. Flipping the end of his hackamore rope around his front feet he drawed 'em together and soon had him hobbled, slipped the hackamore and blind on him, and while the snubber held the snorting head close to his saddle horn, Flint eased and had his double rigging on him to stay. He pulled up on his shap belt, drawed his hat down and in another second he'd slipped into the saddle. The snubber handed him the hackamore rein, the blind was jerked off and the fireworks started.

The fireworks was mostly like crooked rockets going up, and earth jarring tons of brick coming down, as the blue turned on his worst. The first few jumps had Flint feeling for his rigging so as to get to sitting and riding. The high, hard hitting, quick and crooked jumps didn't let up, but with all of that, it seemed like by miracle, Flint found his saddle again. He hadn't lost a stirrup during the first eruptions nor had he grabbed leather, so he was safe so far from having his name scratched off the list, and the riding he put on from then on with such a good hard horse to give him a chance to show his ability left that name with a A Number 1 in front of it. The top of the 7L riders.

There was a couple more 7L riders done good rides and that ended Sol's list for the bucking horse doings. Crockett of the ⅄ then took his place, begin calling his boys one by one and the riding went on with the ⅄ rough string. He had two more riders than Sol did but even at that they didn't average as good altogether as Sol's men did, all excepting for one who put up as good a ride on as tough a horse as Flint did. He was a little center-fire Oregon buckaroo and there was a A No. 1 put in front of his name also.

Davis of the —A was next, his riders also using the outfit's own rough string, good horses and good riding averaging well with Crockett's but not as good as Sol's and he didn't have a rider to compare with either Flint or the Oregon buckaroo, the only two A No. 1's amongst over thirty who rode, and all the way thru, Sol had the best riders, and one of his men was up and decided on for the second prize. But there was too much of a tie between the two up for the first prize to let it go at that, even tho, all the way thru Sol had won. So, to make a final and satisfactory decision it was decided to have the two winning cowboys ride again. Davis had of course lost out on that bet.

Sol and Crockett picked out the best, or worst horses out of each their own rough string, and the reride went on. Flint's horse was another rangy one, a sidewinding, sunfishing, kicking bucker, about as hard a kind there is to ride if not the hardest. But even tho the hard-twisting jumps wasn't at all regular and sometimes like three pitched into one, Flint's flat quirt played a rhythm as it popped on the horse's bowed neck near every time he hit the ground. Very few times did the popping miss, and on such a crooked horse that went a long ways to the good of the ride.

Flint made a great ride, and when the snubber rode alongside and picked up the pony's head before he quit bucking and started stampeding the A No. 1 mark was still by his name.

The Oregon buckaroo's horse was as tough a one as Flint's was, only a different kind of a bucker again, more of a spinner and acted as he'd fall back after each spin, which caused the rider to loosen up on his rigging and put him at a disadvantage for the hard jolts that would follow on. But he rode mighty well, and considering all, even a little better than Flint did, so the judges thought, but considering again, this Oregon buckaroo was riding a center-fire rig which makes it much easier to ride a bucking horse with, it sits more forward on a horse's back and where it misses a lot of hard kinks, where with a double rig it's clamped down to where the rider gets every snapping jolt going and a coming. So taking that under consideration the judges figured that the Oregon buckaroo couldn't done so well on Flint's double rig. Then again, Flint scratched once in a while and used his quirt steady, where the Oregon rider didn't do neither. But all around it was hard to decide, so hard that when the judges gave their decision they left it open for Sol and Crockett to change it. Their decision was A No. 1 for both riders, again a tie.

Old Sol more than reared up at that. "Not by a damsite!" he bellered. "I will agree that it was pretty close riding but if you won't be partial you will say that Flint done a little the best. Besides, all the way thru," he says to Crockett, "my boys outrode yours even if you had two more than I did."

"But that part don't count," says Crockett. "It was the one best rider of each outfit, not all of 'em put together."

"Well, anyhow," Old Sol went on, "that ought to be

considered and I still can't see where the last ride our boys made was a tie. You better admit it, Crockett, when you know doggone well you're beat."

There was a little more discussing on the subject, but finally, again leaving it to the judges, it was agreed that Sol had won, not only all the way thru but even to the last ride.

"But I'll get you on the roping," Crockett comes back at Sol, taking his losing good natured. He more or less had to.

"All right," says Sol, "we'll see, but don't forget you've got Davis to contend with too, and from what I heard of his ropers he'll sure be some contender."

"Yep," agreed Davis. "I think this'll be where I come in."

It had taken a couple of hours to go thru the bucking horse riding, settling on the decision and all, and now the steer roping was next. With that it was decided to give the boys who was on dayherd shift for that morning a chance to see and get in on the doings. Four riders would do with each herd for the time they'd have to hold 'em, and so, four of the boys from the 7L and four from the ↶ who'd seen the bucking horse doings and wasn't named down for the roping was sent out to relieve the six that was with each herd, and then relieved boys soon come a loping in, all but the two who was sort of shy of the sheriff and the law in general. They was good riders and ropers too.

Counting them, all but ten out of over sixty riders would be in at the doings, the most of 'em taking their turn at roping and the rest at witnessing while helping hold the herd. The cooks and flunkies having no way of getting over to the stock herd and where the roping would of course be held would all ride over in the wood wagon that'd been driven from that outfit that morning and they'd have as good a chance at seeing the doings from that wagon as the cowboys would on their horses.

The horses of the rough strings separated and each string taken back to the remudas of the outfits they belonged to by the wranglers, the cowboys, the bosses, the judges and the cooks all moved on to where Davis' stock herd was being loose herded and to grazing. A "cut" (cut out bunch) of mostly cows and big calves was left out about half a mile from the main herd and to be used as a lead for a steer to hit for when cut out of the main herd to be roped.

Like with the bucking horse riding, there was no set rules as to the roping. A steer would be cut out of the main herd and as the steer got out in the clear and headed for the cut the roper was to give him a fifty yard lead, or pass over the line between the two judges before starting. (The judges was about a hundred yards apart on the line and the line was a deep cattle trail.) One extra throw was allowed each roper if the first one was missed, and it didn't matter how he roped or tied his steer so long as he got his down, the tie was good and would stay. It was all up to that and to the time it took as to who would be the winner, and this judging would be much easier than with the bucking horse doings.

Some of the cowboys went to holding the main herd while a few held the cut, and then two men rode into the herd to begin cutting out a good fast steer as the roper, with loop unlimbered and ready, held his horse still on the outside of the herd, to within a guessed hundred feet of the line and waiting for the steer to cross that line, for he wasn't to start his horse until the steer did cross it. The three bosses and some more of the cowboys sort of formed a wing or fence on both sides from the herd where the steer would be cut out and so he'd be sure to hit for the cut.

All was ready, and this time, being it was his herd, Davis was the first to get his men out for the doings. Taking his stand with the list of them in one hand and his watch and reins in the other he called out the first name, for his cowboy to be ready. Then as that cowboy rode up and took his place and the two cowboys in the herd was given the sign, a lean and lanky "Mexico buckskin" was eased thru the herd and when at the edge, a quick jump from the two riders, a pop of the quirt on shap leg and the wild steer shot out like a bullet. There was no turning back, and when he crossed the cow trail line and the roper jumped his horse after him and the steer seen the cut, he hit for it like a prairie dog hits for his hole, for protection in getting in the middle and mixing with that other herd, the cut.

It took a mighty fast horse to catch up to within roping distance of him, but the roper was riding a fast horse, for at them times there'd already been thoroughbreds shipped in and crossed with the mustangs, and the cross made a better and tougher breed than the thoroughbred and they was near as fast. This first roper, like with most of the ropers that would follow, was riding a half breed, and that pony more than et up the distance between him and that fast steer.

But even at that the steer was near over two thirds of the way to the cut before the roper could catch up to within roping distance of him, and then, with his forty foot whaleline, he made a fast and perfect throw over both horns. Now was when a fast horse was needed, to pass the steer as the roper flipped his rope's slack over his rump to go on "yander" and "bust" (throw) him. The horse was fast enough and the busting was well done, for as the horse passed him and the steer went to turn behind, the rope drawed up under his hind quarters, raised him in the air a few feet and flipped him to hit the ground broadside and hard, with his head under him. He hardly no more than landed when the roper was off his horse, by the steer and with his "piggin string" (short tie-down rope) soon had him tied to stay. Then the roper's hat went up for the count of time.

At that the judges and the three bosses was quick to look at their watches to see how many seconds it had taken from the time the steer crossed the line till he was roped and tied and the roper raised his hat and hands. The cowboy had done very good time, considering that there wasn't much practice and such roping to be done with the average day's work on the range, and none of it was done unless necessary. The judges rode over to the tied down steer to inspect the tying and see that it would hold. It was good tying and the roper done the roping and tying from starting line to finish in thirty seconds flat. Davis felt proud and happy and sure that no other cowboy in either of the two other outfits could beat that time.

And that comes out true, for neither of the other two outfits did beat that time. Quite a few come mighty near, to within a few seconds, and made Davis hold his breath. He took a long breath when all the roping was over and his cowboy's time hadn't been beat. But even tho that one cowboy had won first prize and all his cowboys together beat the other two outfits when the time of each cowboy was added up, Davis lost out on the second prize, and the queer part of it was that, again, one of Old Sol's cowboys and one of Crockett's came to a tie, the same as had happened with the bucking horse riding. Both cowboys had roped and tied down their steers in thirty two seconds flat, not a split second's difference. The three bosses had to laugh at that, and

Crockett had to remark to Old Sol: "Well," he says, "it looks like I have about as good a bunch of cowboys as you have."

"Yes, about," grins Sol, "but not quite."

There'd been a few different throws brought with the roping, like the "Johnnie Blocker," where the loop is sailed to spin in front of the steer and slams back faster than the steer can dodge. That throw can't be made for very far and is used mostly when a steer is crowded and is about to stop sudden and dodge back. Then there was that swift throw where the loop is whirled once or twice and slides off the thumb at the speed of a bullet, a good throw if it can be done and a couple of the boys did. But the regular overhead whirling loop and straight throw was the mostly used.

The "dally" men, the ones who take turns around the saddle horn with their rope instead of tying it, didn't come in on the roping, because dally men seldom "bust" (throw) a critter, they work in pairs when it comes to roping, one "heads" (ropes the head), then the other "heels" (ropes the hind feet) and stretches the critter to lay on the side, for branding or whatever is wanted when an animal is roped.

Being there was so few dally men there was no special doings for them, and being that dallying is a hard trick of its own few dally men will even tackle handling a tied rope, for that has quite a few tricks too and some dangerous ones, even with the cowboy who knows how. So, with the tie-men there'd been some rough goings on during the roping. Some big steers was "busted," raised high off the ground and turned over at the end of the rope before they hit the earth to lay for the tying, a few horns was broke in the falls, and a few necks cracked, but as good luck would have it not a neck or leg was broke during the doings, with near forty head of the wild steers being roped.

But even as lucky as it was, the steers wasn't the only ones that took a little rough and tumble. There was some horses jerked down by the fast and heavy steers, and to land hard on their sides or over backwards. Then there was the cowboys, a few had to do some tall scrambling so's their horses wouldn't fall on 'em, also keep out of the dangerous and entangling coils of their ropes as their horses was jerked down. A couple of the horses got on their feet again with the rope between their legs, and being the rope was tied hard and fast to the saddle horn and a tough wild steer at the other end there was considerable commotion when that happened. A bucking, fighting horse at one end of the rope and the same with the steer at the other end. Any place along that rope wouldn't be no place for a cowboy to be at such a time, for them ropes have a great way of coiling around a feller's neck or body once in a while.

Like did happen with one of the boys. His horse went to bucking soon as he made his catch and the rope tightened.

The horse bucked in a circle one way and the steer bellered around another way, no chance for the cowboy to keep the slack of the rope off himself, there was no slack to draw up on, for the rope was kept tight as the whirling and bucking went on and the cowboy rode. And that cowboy had to ride, for the first thing he knew as his horse went to whirling and bucking there was a couple of coils of the rope around his waist and saddle horn, and holding him there, a wild steer's weight at one end tied to a bucking horse at the other end and the cowboy with coils of the rope around his waist in between.

He'd of been near cut in two, or badly hurt, but soon seeing what was going on a couple of cowboys raced up, one caught the horse and pulled his head up, while the other cut the rope.

There was other kinds of happenings, such as many can happen with a rope when there's a wiry steer at one end a horse at the other, a cowboy in the middle and all for him to handle. All was more or less dangerous happenings, for roping is dangerous anyway, even if all goes well, but with that there was some happenings that was also comical, like when one cowboy roped and throwed his steer in good time and went to tie him down. The steer hadn't been throwed hard enough to lay, got up as the cowboy come near and, letting out a beller, went after him. Naturally the cowboy run for his horse, not only to get away from the steer but to get in the saddle and throw him again, but the horse not being any too gentle (or such as the well trained rope horses used in Rodeos nowdays are) turned and started to run too, away from the cowboy and the same way the steer was coming, with the cowboy in the middle, the horse ahead and the steer close behind him.

Well, at that turn of events the cowboy soon seen he had no chance in that race, but for a cowboy he was sure running good, and then, when the steer's long horns was about a foot from him was when he quit the race. He dodged quick and away to one side and fell flat to earth, the steer's head was jerked with the rope at about that time which kept him from turning, and for a ways he had to follow the horse at rope's length. The cowboy was now safe.

There was some more goings on before the herd was left to the dayherd men to let scatter and graze again and which wasn't with the doings. One Mexican vaquero (cowboy) took after one long legged steer that quit the herd like for never to return, but as that vaquero got near he run his horse right into him, horse's shoulder against steer's rump, and in such a way that the steer was sort of lifted into the air, twisted and was throwed to turn a couple of good hard somersaults.

When the steer got up on his feet he was kind of dizzy and hardly knew where he was at, and when he finally located the herd he seemed in a hurry to get back to it. But that vaquero wasn't thru yet and before that herd-quitting steer got to it he turned him over once more. When that steer did get to the herd after that he got right into the middle of it. He would never quit it again.

That's a very hard stunt to do and a rider has to break a horse to it before it can be done. But not to be bested, and as another wiry steer broke out, for no reason only that he maybe felt wild, another rider took after him and that steer was also stood on his head and made to turn over a couple of times. With this second rider, who was none other than Flint, he didn't just bump the steer as the Mexican vaquero did, which in itself was plenty hard to do, but he grabbed a hold of the steer's tail, took a couple of turns around the saddle horn with it as the horse bumped and passed him, and that way the herd-quitting steer was well stood on his head and turned over a couple of times, to later on get up again, look around kind of foolish and like wondering what'd happened. That steer was also glad to get back into the herd.

Today's rodeos are not allowed to put on such doings, not even steer roping it for throwing. It's of course not so necessary because there's plenty of action and goings on without that, but on the range, where the cattle are not of the mild eyed breed that comes home to the name of Bossie or the rattling of a bucket, it's often very necessary to herd-break the wildest so they will stay with the herd and can be handled. If left break away as their wild instinct tells 'em, they soon would get so they couldn't be drove or held into a herd, corralled or shipped. They'd get wild, others would follow their lead and in time they'd have to be shot down like game. Then this beef eating nation would suffer considerable.

The doings now all over, the cattle left to scatter and peacefully grazing again, the cooks and flunkies in the wagon hit for camp, the —A camp this time, and proceeded to mix and cook the grub for the noon meal, for it was near that time. On account of there being so many and not enough dishes to go around, there'd have to be a relay on that meal. The 7L and ⅍ riders and cooks would of went to their own camps, but this was a gathering that very seldom happened and needed a little visiting. Besides, Davis would be moving his herd on right after that meal and make camp again some miles further on before night come.

After a while the three bosses and the two judges come slowly riding to camp while discussing that forenoon's doings. The riders then drifted in by twos and fours, all doing the same, and some just plain visiting or talking of where one or the other would hit for when shipping was done. Wether to stay with the outfit for the winter or to drift on to some other cow-country state where there was no snow to buck was sometimes brought in on the talk, till, as all hit camp and hobbled or picketed their horses, and when all being together that way the talk got more general, then the two judges left the 3 bosses and went to join the cowboys who now had gathered in bunches and sort of formed a circle around the blazing fire. For this was another cold fall day. . . .

It had been made understood with the cowboys that the men who was to relieve that forenoon's dayherd men, for all three of the herds, was to eat first, also with the wranglers, the three bosses and the two judges, for the judges would have to get back to town, and two of the bosses to see about the cars they'd ordered. The rest of the men would have plenty of time to eat and visit afterwards.

Soon enough there was a holler from the Davis cook to "come and get 'er," and the ones to eat first begin to make tracks for the chuck box panel for tin plates, cups and utensils. The rounds was made to the Dutch ovens, skillets and coffee pot on coals by the fire, and after another trip to the chuck box for seasoning and such they finally all trailed back to their fire and to squat cross legged around it, full plate between the knees and coffee cup on the ground by the side.

There was little talk during the meal amongst the cowboys, for being they was to relieve the men on dayherd, and it was cow country custom that no time should be wasted, none wanted to be last. The wranglers also had to each get their remuda corralled for a change of horses for all hands before change of shifts, and they wasn't wasting no time mixing talk with eating either. . . . The big fun was over.

THIRD STORY

WINTER MONTHS IN A
COW CAMP

I T TOOK ME a long time to figger out anywheres near
of what I'd done with my summer's wages. I know I'd
bought me a few winter clothes and paid out for a
couple of weeks of livery stable board for my horse; then
the hotel bill besides some real fancy meals had took a lot
of my money. I'd bought the rounds when my turn came
and stepped out with the boys, and even though I was breathing sober steady ever since I hit town, I couldn't for the life
of me make out how that money went so fast. I'd saved it
careful too that summer before, even rode my old saddle
and made it do till the shipping was done so I could manage
to live a life of ease for the few winter months.

Riding them winter months didn't strike me as anything
cheerful no more, and I thought that this once I'd be able
to hole in comfortable for that snowy cold period; but my
pockets sprung a leak, and being that I couldn't get no comfort of what was past and spent, I begins to look into the
future and wonders what cow outfit would hire a cowboy
this time of year. I'm running the irons of the outfits I know

of through my mind and looking into the future real deep, when I raises up straight in my bed and looks out of the hotel window to see snow coming down and adding up on the fourteen inches already on the level. Yep! I figgers the range will be needing riders.

I finds myself whistling some as I clean up, and somehow and another when I comes down the steps into the hotel lobby it don't look like much to me. There's a few tinhorn gamblers with the "hop head" complexion sticking around, and a couple of fat slick-looking gents a-swapping jokes by the big stove. I sashays out in the dining room, where I figgers on throwing a bait to hold me till I reaches my next stopping place.

My ham and eggs is down to half when old Tom Meyers, superintendent of the "hip-O," steps up and asks how I'm setting. "Pretty fair," I says and don't tell him none of my plans, thinking that he's full handed anyway. I don't show where I'm at all interested when he says he's needing of a man at "Stone Pile" camp. "It's mean weather out right now," I says, "and I'm afraid I'm getting kinda soft, but how much are you paying?"

With a month's wages handed to me in advance I pays my bills at the hotel and stable and it feels kinda good to be riding out again even if the snow was deep and more of it was coming. My horse was a sniffing of it and lining out full of life. After the long spell in the stall he was glad to be out and going somewhere, and somehow I wasn't a bit sorry either.

A couple of days and along what I figgered to be about sundown (it was still snowing and the wind was coming up) I reaches the camp where I'm to get my winter horses and ride from. There's three or four rolls of bedding belonging to boys what'd *stayed to town* for the winter same as I'd figgered on doing and I uses one of 'em till I can get my own roll.

There's two ranch hands at the camp shovelling hay to near a thousand head of "hospital cattle" (weak stock), besides a cook and a rider not counting me, and the next morning when I sniffs and smells the bacon from my bunk I know that I've settled down to some tall hard work.

It's still dark when I saddles my horse and lines out. I'd rode that country many times before and knowed how and where the cattle was running. The dry stock was in good condition, outside the few old stuff and cows with calves and "leppies" (orphant calves) what are to be brought in and fed.

Along about noon I have a few bunches spotted what had weak ones in and starts back to camp, cutting 'em out as I go and driving 'em along making about a mile an hour. Them being weak and the snow being deep it ain't long till they begin to get tired, and me knowing that the less I rush 'em the better time I'll make, I'm driving 'em easy and keeps 'em just barely moving. As the driving is kept up and the cattle want to rest they begin to spread like a fan, heading all directions, and I have a hard time keeping 'em together; but taking it real easy manages to get 'em a half a mile closer to camp, when a couple of dogies on the outside begin to get on the "prod" (fight), which means it's time for me to quit.

I had twelve head in that bunch and it took me six hours to drive 'em about five miles. It was way after dark when I dropped 'em and hit for camp, and I still had a good ten miles to go.

It takes me three days to bring 'em in, and the end of the third and late again finds me pushing a mighty weak, tired bunch of dogies through the gates of the feed yard at the camp and headed for the big shelter sheds. Half of 'em was wanting to fight but when they see the hay what was spread and waiting for 'em they kind of forgot I was around and went to eating.

For a spell that kind of work kept on. There was days when we'd be drifting with the herds and the blizzard a-howling full force, when you could hardly see your hand in front of you and the only way you knowed the direction you was headed was by the wind. If that wind switched to another direction without you knowing of it (you wasn't apt to know in the blinding storm) you was running good chances of getting lost unless you run acrost some landmark what told of your whereabouts.

The snow drifted and piled high but in drifting it cleared some ridges, and there's where the strong cattle along with the range horses was finding their feed.

Then the weather cleared and stayed a steady cold. Me and the other cowboy had covered the whole country and hazed in all what needed feed; riding was getting easy.

And one day when we hear of a dance what was going to be pulled off at the crossing we figger there could be no better time for it to happen; so saddling up our private ponies us two boys and the cook set out for the crossing forty miles away. Too bad the ranch hands couldn't come, being they had to shovel so much hay *every day*, no more and no less, but they was good enough to let the cook go, remarking that if they couldn't get away they wouldn't keep anybody else from it.

We covered that forty miles and got to the other end in plenty time for the big midnight feed. We had our ears all wrapped up to keep 'em from freezing off, but, along with the coyotes howling to the moon, we could hear old

Darb a-see-sawing on his fiddle and somebody else calling the dance a half a mile before we reached the house.

Lights was in every room and the smoke was coming straight up through three different chimneys; so we spurred up our ponies and rode towards the stack yards where we turned 'em loose.

We just enters the house as we hear a "tag" dance announced and by the time our chaps, spurs, and extra clothes are took off it's half over, but not too late to tag a couple of hombres, take their ladies, and dance some till *we* got tagged ourselves. When the dance was through the blood was beginning to circulate some, and by the time we shook hands all around we was more than ready to help keep things cheerful.

Half the crowd was cow-punchers from everywhere, a few cowmen with their families, from the oldest down to the weaner, what was left in the bedroom but made itself heard now and again, and a few boys from town what sleighed over and brought a few girls along. There was about six men to each lady, and it was always a wonder to me how the supposed to be weaker sex could tire the men even at that, but they did, and the fatter they was the longer they stayed.

The big feed at midnight and specially that coffee was a life saver to most of us what come in late; and when the fiddler resumed his playing there was no quitting till daybreak. The ladies all disappeared then, and us boys would take the floor and go on with the stag dance. That stag dance was apt to be kind of rough and end up in wrestling matches.

Games and tricks of all kinds are tried; none are easy but some are done, and when that lags down there may be two young fellers in the corner what'd been arguing or betting

on riding; more bets are put in from the outside crowd just to make things interesting.

The bunch all heads for the corrals and a wall-eyed rangy bronc is led out, saddled, straddled, and with the bawling of that bronc bucking away with a whooping rider fanning him, the crowd hollering "stay with him, cowboy" or the like, the sun is coming up, the ladies are waking, and the end of the doings have come.

Breakfast is spread and all hands, after partaking of the bait, are talking of hitting the trail. Ponies are caught, harnessed or saddled, and with a lot of howdedo the crowd is leaving for their home grounds.

My bronc was "high-lifed" as I go through the corral gate and bucks right through the calf pen, same as it wasn't there, near hooking on the corner of the stable as he goes by; but a mile further on he cools down some and the boys catch up with me.

We're riding along a ways, when Dan remarks, "I feel something in the air." A light breeze had sprung up from the west, and come to think about it, it felt a whole lot as if a chinook was headed our way, and as we ride on that breeze keeps a-getting warmer and stronger. The deep snow was already beginning to show the effects and sagging as the warm wind et its way through.

The next day as I ride out of camp the chinook is blowing for sure, and when I strikes the first bunch of cattle I found them to be as I was afraid I would. They'd been strong and rustling fine a few days before; they'd been on their feet steady through the cold weather, not hankering to lay down in the snow, and the exercise kept the blood circulating; but the chinook had took the snow off a few spots on the ridges and at them spots is where I finds most of the stock laying

down and all the life out of 'em.

They was hardened to the cold and the sudden warmth left 'em so weak that only half of 'em can get up as I rides in on 'em. I spends a couple of hours helping the weakest ones by "tailing 'em up," and steadying 'em some afterwards so they can navigate. I'm working hard 'cause I know that when the chinook quits blowing and it gets cold again them cattle what are down now will get stiff and cramped, the blood'll quit circulating, and the critters' legs will be plumb useless, which leaves 'em good only for coyote bait.

"Tailing up" is an awful hard and ungrateful job too, the critter treats you the same as if you was a bear or a wolf what's come to eat her alive, and proceeds to try and hook you, and, wild-eyed, bellers in your ear how she'd like to tear you up. You help her along and she struggles to get on her feet, not so that she might be able to rustle and live but just to get a chance to run you down. Sometimes she works hard enough that she forgets what she was going to do when she did get on footing again, and if you can sneak away using her body to keep her from seeing you and get on your horse before she sees, everything may be O. K.; but, if she happens to turn her head and glance back as you're making your getaway, she might remember what she wanted to do to you a while ago *and try it*. She'll let out a bellering war whoop and forget that she's kinda shaky in the knees, and is apt to turn and try to get to you too quick, which makes her do a spraddling nose dive. Down again, and there to stay unless you help her up once more and make a success of your getting away.

I've tailed up one critter as often as half a dozen times before I could leave without her taking after me and falling down again. Then I'd have to hang my coat, when I had one with me, over her horns and blindfold her that way till I'd get to my horse. Once in the saddle I'd ride by her, get the coat back and be away before she'd know what happened.

Well, I kept a-riding the bare ridges that day and getting cattle on their feet and moving. The next day was the same and the chinook was still a-blowing and eating up the snow. Half of it is already melted away and water is running down the coulees to the creeks, making 'em the size of rivers. Any stranger would of thought sure that spring'd come sudden, but I knowed the cowmen was losing sleep for worrying, more afraid of the harm the hard freeze would do to the stock after the chinook'd left than the chinook itself could do while it was blowing.

Along about the middle of the afternoon I meets with the other rider; I sees he's near all in as he pulls up his horse and goes to rolling a smoke, but he's smiling some as he remarks that these winter jobs sure do get aggravating at times. We had pretty well all of our cattle up and a-going

again and it was about time, 'cause we could feel the air getting cooler and the breeze was shifting to the north. The
snow'd quit melting and the creeks was getting down to creek
size again. "I'm thinking tonight is going to put a crimp in
some of the stock," Dan says as we start out for some draws
to the west where we figgered to find the few bunches of
cattle we'd missed in our circles.

It's good and dark by the time we head our horses towards
camp and it was getting colder every minute. The wet snow
was freezing through solid and in lots of places the top crust
would hold our horses. "I wouldn't be surprised," I says,
"but what the Old Man (meaning the superintendent) might
have to either ship the stock south to pull 'em through the
winter, that is if they can make it to the railroad, or else ship
some feed in and haul it out here to 'em; that would be some
expensive too. The bad shape the range is in now with all
the good feed buried in solid ice, something'll sure have to
be done or else the outfit'll find itself with more cowboys
than cattle when spring does come."

"Sure," Dan says, "and for my part I wouldn't mind hitting south with the stock 'cause I feel like I could stand some
warmer climate myself." And rubbing his ears he puts his
horse into a lope remarking that we'd better be drifting if
we want anything to eat that's warm.

The Cypress Cattle Company was running over thirty
thousand head of cattle; three thousand of 'em was at Stone
Pile camp, where Dan and me was ridin, the rest was at
other cow-camps, and a big herd at the home ranch, where
there was other riders and hay shovellers looking after 'em.
At our camp there was enough hay put up the summer before to feed and pull through the winter about fifteen hundred head of stock. The other fifteen hundred was supposed

to rustle. They could easy enough and come out strong in the spring after any average winter, 'cause the stock what was left out on the range to rustle through was all dry stuff and steers. Cows with calves and weaners and all old or weak stock was fed from the start of the bad weather till spring breakup.

The weather kept clear and cold; the little glass tube outside our camp by the door was saying from thirty to thirty-five below, and had been keeping that up for about a week. Lucky, we thought, the wind wasn't blowing then or every critter would of froze stiff where they stood. We kept on bringing in the weakest and only them what really needed feed the most. There was many more should been brought in but the last week made us fill the feed yards, so that it wouldn't be wise to bring them in. There was enough hay to feed fifteen hundred head till spring and it was better, we thought, to keep on feeding just them and take a chance on letting the stronger pull through on the outside, than feed two thousand or more and run out of hay at the wrong time and lose 'em all.

It didn't look like there was going to be any shipping done either way. No super or cow boss showed up to see how the stock was coming and we figgered that old timers like they was, and never forgetting the days when there wasn't a hoof fed, they'd decided to take a chance like they'd done many a winter before and hope that the weather would change in some way in time to save the stock. And as luck would have it the weather did change.

It was near three weeks since the chinook'd come and left the range a field of ice and crusted snow with the few bare spots that helped some keeping the cattle alive. The willows on the creek bottoms and the sage was all et down to the ice, and, outside of the few branches what was too big for them to tackle, the country was clean as a whistle. There was little bunches of range horses here and there and even though they was having a hard time of it, it was some easier for them 'cause they could paw out their feed where the critter could only root with her nose. But along the trails the horses would make where they pawed up the hard snow and broke the crust with their hoofs, you could see the cattle following and picking what the horses would leave.

Big hunks of crusted snow had been pawed out and turned up for the feed underneath, but as they was loosened the grass came out with the hunks and left only bare ground.

The stock had so little feed in 'em that it looked like their flanks was near touching the backbone, but the most of 'em was strong and if it hadn't been for that chinook they would now be in good shape.

Anyway the weather changed and for the best. We didn't think it for the best at first 'cause the change was for *another chinook* and they as a rule don't leave nothing but bone piles unless they come late in the spring, and this was only February. For forty-eight hours it blowed warm. Dan and me was doing our bestest riding, and tailing up for all we was worth every critter what had to be helped on her feet. We'd remark that it'd be for the last time 'cause we was sure afraid of what the cold that 'most always follows a chinook would do to 'em.

It started clouding up before the chinook quit, and that's when our hopes come back. The snow was 'most all gone to water and running down the draws; the country was left bare and brown and the cattle weaker than ever, but feed a-plenty was in sight and easy to get at, and clouding up as it was with the wind dying down gives us to understand that there won't be no real cold weather coming right soon anyway.

It stayed warm and in a couple of days it started to snow, kinda wet at first, but she stuck and kept on a-coming, slow but sure and steady. The cloudy weather was with us for a good two weeks and gradually getting colder, when it cleared again and the thermometer went down to ten below. There was near a foot of snow on the ground again and the cattle was having a hard time rooting down to the feed, but the slow drop of the thermometer and the chance at some feed before the snow came recuperated 'em some. A few more had to be brought in and we did it, taking big chances of running out of hay too soon.

And then another six inches of snow piled up on top of the foot already down, which makes us and the hay shov-ellers do a heap of figgering as to how we was going to pull the stock through. The hay was fed and handled real care-ful but it was dwindling away fast; two thousand of the hungry critters was in the feed pens eating up the hay what was supposed to carry not over fifteen hundred head.

And by all appearances it looked like the "hospital stuff" would have to be fed another six weeks before we could call 'em pulled through. Dan and me was doing our darnedest not to bring in any more than we could help and coaxing 'em along to stand up and rustle where they was, but there was times right along every day when we'd have to come in with a few more.

Spring was late, it still looked like the middle of winter, and we had to contend not only with the usual few winter calves but spring calves was beginning to pop up here and there and showing their little white faces. The daggone coy-otes was the only animal getting fat, and it sure used to do my heart a lot of good to keel one of 'em over just when he'd be doing some tall sneak on some poor little feller of a calf when his mammy was too far away or too weak to get there in time to do any protecting.

Like one day riding along and keeping tab on the weak ones as usual, I runs across a cow-track in the snow. A little baby calf was trying mighty hard to keep up with her and a little further on there's two other kinds of tracks joins in and follows. They're big tracks, too big for coyotes, and I concludes they must be gray wolves. Now I know that as a rule wolves wouldn't tackle them only maybe just for the want to kill, or when horses is getting scarce.

Anyway, I know *I* sure like to get 'em *any time I can* no matter what they're after, and spurs up on the trail, the 30–30 carbine right in my hands and the business end of it pointed straight ahead. Daggone 'em, they *are* after that cow and calf. I can see that plain enough by the signs in the snow where she'd stopped, made a stand and went on for some place, I figgered, where she could back up alongside a cliff or something and have only one side to watch from.

I can see the wolves are only after a little excitement 'cause they could of killed both her and the calf right there and then if they'd wanted to. Instead, they just let her go and kept on aggravating her as she went. I thought to myself if they're so rearing for excitement, I'd sure be glad to oblige 'em that way when I catches up.

The trail heads on for the foot-hills; I'm keeping my horse into a high lope, and slacks up only when topping ridges, so I won't bump into the little party and queer things before I can get into action. I want to see them before they see me.

I finally spots 'em a half a mile to the right. There's a ridge between us, and soon as I get a peek of their whereabouts and the lay of the land, what little I showed of myself is out of sight again. I seen where the mother'd found a good spot to make her *last stand*, and, even tho' she knowed how the fight was going to end, she was sure making use of the rim-rock she'd backed up against, and bellering for help that didn't seem to come.

Hell bent for election I follows up the draw I'm in to where I figger I'd better hoof it the rest of the way. There was no wind to give me away, and I manages to crawl up to within fifty yards of the fighting bunch, taking in at a glance all what'd been going on while I'm looking down the rifle sights.

The wolves are enjoying themselves so much that they're not on the look-out as they generally are. They had the cow down and letting her last as long as they could without allowing the fight to get too monotonous. Her head and horns are still a-going and mighty dangerous to anything what comes near. The poor little calf was all together as yet, and off a ways, plumb helpless and watching, too young to know for sure what to do. The wolves had figgered him not worth while to fool with right then. They'd fix his mammy first, spend a few minutes with him afterwards, and then go on to the next victim.

And right there I stopped one of 'em with a bullet right through him from shoulder to shoulder. The other started to run and I lets him have a pill too, but he kept on a-running, dragging two useless hind legs; his back was broke. A couple more shots what don't seem to affect him none and I gets my horse, takes after him, and brings him back, limp, with a bullet between his ears.

I gathers up little Johnny (calf), puts his dying mammy out of misery, and being I'm not very far from camp, I don't

stop to skin the wolves right then but takes 'em in as they are. Tying their hind legs together I throws 'em over the back of the saddle, gets on myself and pulls the little "leppy" up in front of me. My horse don't quite agree to all the load and specially objects to wolves, but I finally talks him into being good enough to take us the little ways to camp.

Two more weeks gone, and it still looks and feels like the middle of winter, when by rights of season the range ought to be getting bare of snow and the grass showing a little green; and worse yet, the hay is all gone and fed up, every speck of it.

There was a little horse hay, but that little bit wouldn't mean nothing to all them hungry cattle, and besides them horses had to work and help save them same cattle, and they had to be well fed to do that work.

So it seems to us that the outfit is up against it for sure. We know that no hay can be bought nowheres around, being they've all got their own stock to save and running short themselves. Dan and me had just about give up thinking of some way out, when of a sudden it comes to me, and I remembers of how one time up in Alberta a cowman saved his stock and pulled 'em through in good shape with a six-horse team and a drag (or snowplough).

No more thought of than tried. There was enough harness in the stables to hook up thirty head of horses, and two teams on hand and ready; but we wanted two six-horse teams to do the work and we was short eight head; so Dan and me hits out looking through every bunch of horses on the range for anything what had collar marks, and any of 'em what had was run in and put to work. It didn't matter whether they belonged to the outfit or not.

Two V-shaped drags was made out of heavy logs with thick planks nailed on the outside so it'd push the snow away on both sides and clean. We get the teams all hooked up, straightened around, and we're ready to go. It worked fine, and the grass wherever we went and drug was easy to get. The snow hadn't drifted any and was no thicker in the draws than on the ridges, so we worked the draws and found plenty of the good strong feed our cattle was needing so bad.

We had to cover a lot of country and keep a-going so that they'd all get some; but the exercise and rustling, along with that feed they was getting, made 'em some stronger, and it wasn't but a few days when the cattle all knowed what them V-shaped logs dragging along meant.

The strongest ones would follow 'em right up for a ways, and we'd come down the same draw but on the other side. The leaders would stop and feed, leaving the weaker cattle have a chance as we come by.

That'd been going on for about two weeks; the stock wasn't picking up no fat but they was making out all right. The ranch-hands handled the drags and Dan and me was riding, still bringing a few weak ones from the outside stuff every once in a while.

May was getting near now and sure enough spring ought to show itself pretty quick if it's going to show up at all; but as Dan remarked to me and says, "Bill, this damn country ain't got no spring or summer to speak of; it's eight months winter and four months cold weather," and I begins to think he was right.

But the days was getting longer and the sun stronger, and pretty soon it begins to get warmer, and after a while I notices at the edge of where the snow'd been scraped off that the grass was getting green. It looked so good that I come near eating some.

Then one morning as I'm saddling up, a light breeze hits me, and it's coming from the southwest. After that it didn't take long; it started to melt and get warm but not so warm that it'd weaken the cattle too much. The snow-plough was put away and instead of bringing in weak stock any more we'd spend our time tailing up what few felt the effects of the coming warm weather.

We was beginning to see little white and brockle-faced calves sunning themselves everywhere and their mammies right close was filling up on the half green buffalo grass, picking up steady on fat and strength.

The gray wolves was hitting out for the tall timber and the coyotes had to be satisfied with gophers once more. Spring had come.

FOURTH STORY

LONE COWBOY

I 'VE OFTEN WONDERED what power keeps drawing a human or animal back to the place where daylight was first blinked at. Many a time a man will go back to the country of his childhood when there's not near as much for him at that home spot as where he just left. I've seen horses leave good grassy range and cross half a state to get to a home range where feed and water was scarce and the country rocky.

The same power must of drawed me, but I was hitting for better country instead of worse when I, so natural like and without thought, drifted to where I first stood up and talked. . . . After I left the ranch and crossed the river, it wasn't but a few days that I begin to notice something mighty familiar about the country. The further South I went the more familiar it got and I begin to feel mighty contented, like as if I was at home and amongst my own folks. There was no people and no landmarks that I recognized to let me know I was in my home grounds, nothing but the general lay of the country itself.

I must of rode down many a draw and over many a bench where my dad's horses had left a hoofprint. I tried to find out just where in that country I was born, but nobody seemed to know and nobody could tell me of my dad. A few had heard of him, but the ten years that'd passed since his death didn't leave much to remember.

It was pretty late spring when one day, down country a ways, I sees a herd a skirting along swale after swale. Scattered out a bit and grazing the way they was, it looked like the whole country was moving. There was only about half a dozen men with that big herd when I first spotted it, but as I rode up on a knoll to get a better look I could see more riders on both sides of me drifting down from all directions and passing the main herd, each rider was bringing along more cattle and was careful not to let 'em mix with the main herd because in the new bunches that was being brought in was many calves that had to be branded. When that was done the new bunches would be throwed in the big herd too, making it still bigger.

I'd seen quite a few big herds of cattle before, but this was the biggest I'd ever seen up till that time. There must of been at least eight thousand head of cattle in the main herd alone. I wondered why they was moving so many cattle at that time of the year. Then I got to thinking that it was on account of wanting to save that part of the range so as the beef herd could be throwed onto it to mature later on. As I found out later, I'd guessed right, and the cattle I seen that day was only a good sized herd as compared to what that one outfit owned.

Further on, down country and past the big herd, I could see the remuda and on a little flat in the creek bottom was the roundup wagon and camp of the outfit.

Leading my pack horse, I fell in with a couple of the riders that was coming in off circle and I helped 'em shove their bunch in to the cutting grounds not far from camp. While riding along with them there was hints dropped that the outfit was short handed. I didn't pay much attention to that because I knowed, even then, that all riders like to see many more come in and hit the foreman for a job, and get it. The more riders there is, the shorter the nightguard shift is cut, and the further apart comes the dayherd shift. Them is two things the cowboy hates to do most, specially day-herding, too slow and monotonous.

Dayherding means grazing and holding a herd in day-time, a herd that's to be shipped or moved to some other part of the range. On a well-run and full-handed cow outfit the dayherd shift comes every two or three days for half a day at the time. Range cattle are not herded only, as I've just said, when a bunch is held to be shipped or moved. There's three shifts in dayherding, morning, afternoon and evening shift. The evening shift is called "cocktail." Two to four men go on them shifts at a time, all depends on the size of the herd that's being held. After the evening shift the night-guard begins, from eight o'clock till daybreak, when each rider takes a shift of from one to two hours (sometimes half the night and more). The last guard is "relieved" by the first dayherd shift.

Many riders like to take a "rep" job (representing a neighboring outfit) because with that job there's no day herding. The reason for that is that the "rep" has to be on the cutting grounds so as to look thru every fresh herd that comes in off every day's "circle" (roundup), cut out and brand the cattle that belongs to his outfit, and throw them in the main herd.

I helped the two riders bring their bunch to the cutting grounds, and being I had a pack horse to contend with, I rode on into camp. I unpacked and unsaddled, but I didn't turn my horses loose because I figgered the wrangler would be bringing in the remuda for a change of horses pretty quick. It's a bad point to turn a horse loose at that time because, being the wrangler has to get *all* the loose horses in, that would only give him the extra work of getting mine, besides the unnecessary corralling of 'em.

I was just unsaddling when a rider which I figgered was the foreman rode into camp. He didn't turn his horse loose either, not till the wrangler run the remuda in the rope corral. There he unsaddled and turned him in with the others. Then all the cowboys rode in, all but a few that was left to hold the cattle that'd been gathered that morning, also the few others that was with the main herd. There must of been at least twenty cowboys with that roundup camp.

The boys got to the chuck box and made the rounds from there to the skillets and ovens for all that was needed to make a meal. After they all was set I started in and done the same. . . . I was still eating when most of the boys was thru, had caught their fresh horses and gone. The "relief" men was the first to go. They rode to take the place of the riders that was with the main herd and the others that was holding the morning's drive. There's fast riding during them reliefs because the men that's relieved still have to eat and change horses and be on the job for the afternoon's work. A "drag" is sure not thought much of in a roundup camp.

There was some mighty good men with that outfit and they was riding some mighty tough horses, tough as a Northern range horse can get, and I got to wondering a bit if I'd better try and get a job there after seeing how some of them

ponies acted. One of the riders had told me that each rider
had three broncs (unbroke horses) in his string, also a
couple of spoiled horses. The rest of the string was made
up of the gentler ones.

I was by the corral as the last men was catching their
horses. The foreman was coiling up his rope when I walked
up to him and asked.

"Are you taking on any more riders?" . . . Just like that.

He looked at me and grinned. "Why yes, Son," he says,
"when I can find any. . . ."

I didn't say anything to that, then after a while he asks.

"Looking for a job?"

"Yessir," I says.

The foreman shook out two coils of his rope and made
a loop.

"I don't know how I'm going to fit you up with a string
of horses," he says, as he looked the remuda over, "but
maybe I can rake up enough gentle ones out of the two
strings that's left. . . . The next rider that comes along and
wants a job will have to be some powerful rider."

On many outfits I've rode for, a string was never split.
Each string was made up of ten or twelve head of horses
for each rider. There was unbroken horses for the short circles (rides), spoiled horses for long circles, good all around
horses for any work, cow horses for dayherd and cutting out,
and then there was the night horses. About two of each of
them horses went to make up a string and ten to twenty
of them strings went to make a remuda. As I said before,
them strings was never split. If a rider quit or was fired the
horses in his string was not used till he come back, or till
another rider took his place.

On a few outfits, instead of scattering unbroke or spoiled

horses amongst the cowboys, they have a couple of riders who take on and ride nothing but them worst ones. Their string is called the "rough string."

The foreman, being short of riders and having a big herd on his hands, split two strings that day and turned eight head of the gentlest over to me. What was left of the two strings could easy been called "rough" by the best riders.

I knowed that by the fact that two of my "gentle" ones bucked me off regular and most every time I rode 'em. Two others was broncs, full grown but little fellers. They was mean to handle while on the ground but I got along all right once I got in the middle of 'em. They couldn't buck very hard. My other four horses was pretty good, if the mornings wasn't too cold or wet. One of 'em was hard to get on to.

At that outfit was where I first got initiated with rough ponies. The others I'd tried to ride before had been just for fun and that makes a big difference. I was handed gentle old horses while "wrangling" for the big outfit to the North, but now I wasn't wrangling no more, I was on circle, day-herd, nightguard and being a regular hand.

I felt mighty proud of that, but I found out right there that there was grief and sweat on the way to any ambition. My string furnished me with plenty of that. Thinking of what horse I had to ride was the cause of me eating mighty light breakfasts and other meals. The thought of what they might do to me sort of made me lose my appetite. I wasn't exactly what you'd call scared, I was just nervous, very nervous.

Then again, the boys kidding me about what this and that horse of mine did to this man and that man, sure didn't help things any, and even tho I knowed they was kidding, the laughs I'd hand back at 'em wasn't what you might call right hearty.

It might be wondered at why I took on a job that was too much for me when there was so many other jobs that I could of started in at easy. But I didn't wonder. I never wondered and I never thought of any other work than what I'd started with at the outfit. There was nothing else in the world mattered to me but what went with a horse, saddle and rope, and when I took on that job I done it unthinking, like as if there was nothing else. There was nothing else, for me.

Of course I could of rode on to some other outfit where I wouldn't have to ride horses that was so rough on me from the start. But, there again, the start would of been slower, and I might of had to take on the wrangling job too. As it was now, I was started as a regular hand, and, outside of the wrangler and the nighthawk, I had the gentlest horses in the outfit to start in with. Of course that outfit had a great reputation of having tough horses, but mine wasn't really tough, only too tough for me that's all. I was too new yet, and too young, and they just played with me. Any grown cowboy could of handled and rode 'em blindfolded and with both arms tied behind his back.

I stayed on with the outfit. I kept a piling on my ponies and they kept a piling me off. Finally and gradual my piling off got to happen less and less often. I was getting to know my horses. After ten years of riding I was learning how to ride, and come a time, as the boys kept a slapping my hands with a quirt so I'd leave go of the saddle horn, that I begin to straighten up in my saddle and to stay.

It wasn't long after that that most of my *nervousness* begin to leave me. I was getting so used to handling and riding my ponies in whatever they done or whichever way they jumped, that I got to fit in natural with the work, like a six-month-old pair of boots. I got so I never thought ahead of time what horse I was to ride next no more and, being so used to things that way and hardened in, my appetite wasn't hindered by any thoughts of any bad horse. The boys begin to quit kidding me about them horses too, because now I was coming back at 'em with laughs that was sure enough hearty.

It took me about a month or so to get the hang of how to set my ponies when I couldn't see their heads. There was two good reasons why it took me so short a time. One was that I'd been amongst the cowboys and riding pretty steady from the time I could walk and riding had got to be a lot more natural to me than walking. The second reason was that them ponies wasn't very hard buckers. Then again, all around me was the best of teachers, the cowboys themselves. They didn't coach me as to how to set, but they done better, they'd laugh at me when I'd buck off and they'd pass remarks.

"You can ride him, Kid," I'd hear one holler just about the time I'd be hitting the ground. . . . What used to make me sore was to have one of the boys come along and pick me up and brush the dirt off my back with a sagebrush and say something like, "You'll ride him next time sure, but you got to stick closer to your riggin'."

Sometimes, when I'd get pretty high up in my saddle, the boys would ride beside me, reach up in the air and set me back in it. "Now, set there and *ride*," they'd holler.

I finally did get to *ride*, specially when the foreman had a talk with me a week or so after I'd started with the outfit. It was during the "cocktail" shift and he was riding along as me and a few of the boys was grazing the herd towards

the "bed grounds." He rode by the side of me and begin saying,

"I think you better catch your private ponies in the morning, Son, and hit back home where you belong. Your dad ought to have plenty enough riding for you, and horses you can ride, too. This string I handed you is a little too tough for a kid like you."

That talk from the foreman layed me out pretty flat for a spell. Finally I came to enough to say, "I haven't got no dad, and no home to go to."

The foreman had figgered that I'd just got wild and run away from the home ranch. . . . Here was another time I had to tell the story of my life. I told it short and quick and there was a funny look in the foreman's eyes when I got thru. As a wind up I added on.

"And if you'll give me a little more time I'll be able to ride 'em, I think."

"But you're all skinned up now," he says.

"Sure," I comes back at him, "anybody is liable to get skinned up."

I know I won out when I seen him grin, and I sure begin to snap out of it from then on. If I ever meant to ride I started in from there and if I got throwed off I sure left marks on my saddle as to how come.

But the foreman had got to watch me pretty close after that talk I'd had with him. Learning that I had no home sort of worried him, and I think he felt like he ought to be some sort of a guardian over me. I caught him trying to swap my best bucker off to the wrangler for a gentler one one day, and I made such a holler that the trade didn't go.

"I rode him easy the last time he bucked," I says, "and, besides, he's in *my* string."

Well, I kept on riding and also kept my string as it was first handed me, and came a time when it was hard for any of them ponies to loosen me. It wasn't so long after that when they couldn't loosen me at all, and then is when I got to thinking I was *some* rider.

But riding wasn't all I was learning while with that out-fit, and, even tho I'd growed up with handling stock pretty well, I learned a lot more there. I wasn't playing now, and I had to be something else besides somebody setting on a horse. I had to know how to find and "shove" cattle while on circle, I had to know where to be at the cutting grounds, what to head off and how. Then I took on calf wrassling while branding was on. Of course I took only little fellers there.

A writer said one time that on account of doing nothing else but riding a cowboy's muscles are not developed, only from the waist down. I never seen a cowboy yet who looked that way, and I'm thinking that if anybody swings a rope for hours at the time, like is done during branding, or wrassles big husky calves for as long, there'll be some exercise found that takes in the whole body, and exercise of the kind where hide-bound muscles would never do, because there's some-thing else besides strength needed in that work.

It's ticklish work at times, such as saddling or handling a mean horse while on the ground, and our horses are not as small as most people think. Few are smaller than the average polo horse, and many size up with the *hunter* of the East. *Wild* horses of that size can jerk a man around pretty well if he don't know how to handle himself. Then while that horse is quivering and about ready to blow up, if any-body is doubtful of the cowboy's shoulder muscles, try and slip forty pounds of our saddle on such a horse's back with one hand. The cowboy does it because he has to hold the horse's head with the other.

With the big herds that was handled on that outfit I had to keep my eyes and ears well opened if I was to do my work right. There was brands to read and tally up on. That, along with making out the earmarks, wartles and vents, was my grammar while I was riding. There was many other things, too, that had to be noticed and which, while only shifting a herd, would take quite a size book to explain.

There was my shift on nightguard where I was bawled out on for getting off my horse too close to the herd. I was bawled out for many things I done now and again but never more than once for any one thing. I always remembered.

I also remember once when I started to sing while on nightguard. I'd started sudden and on a pretty high note and come daggone near causing a good stampede. There's writers who say that cowboys sort of sing cattle to sleep and sing on nightherd only for that reason. That strikes me funny, specially when I think of how I near caused a stampede by doing just that. If a cowboy sings on nightherd it's only because he wants to, and not at all to sing any cattle to sleep. Sometimes, on real dark and spooky nights, a rider will hum or sing or whistle while going around the herd, but that's only so they'll know of his coming and won't scare as they might if they didn't see him till he got near.

Well . . . the herds was shifted, the cattle was graded and throwed on the range they belonged. I done my little best to be of some help and, outside of wanting to "push" the cattle too hard and dragging a rope, which I got bawled out for some more, I think I made a pretty fair hand of myself. Anyway, I'd got so I could ride my horses. But "that's nothing," said the cowboys, "you've only been riding *pets*."

FIFTH STORY

SMOKY, THE RANGE COLT

S MOKY DIDN'T SEE the first light of day through a box-stall window and there was no human around to make a fuss over him and try to steady him on his feet for the first few steps. Smoky was just a little range colt, born on the wide prairie, and all the company he had that first morning of his life was his watchful mammy.

Smoky wasn't quite an hour old when he began to take an interest in things. The warm spring sun was doing its work and kept a pouring warmth right through his little body. Pretty soon his head came up kind of shaky and he began nosing around his own long front legs that were stretched out in front of him. His mammy was close by him, and, at the first move the colt made, she ran her nose along his short neck and nickered softly. Smoky's head went up another two inches at the sound and his first little answering nicker was heard.

That was the starting of Smoky. Pretty soon his ears began to work back and forth towards the sound his mammy would make as she moved. He was trying to find out just where she was. Then something moved right in front of his nose, it had been there quite a spell but his vision was a little dim yet. That something moved again and planted itself still closer. He took a sniff at it. It was one of his mammy's legs. His ears pricked up and he tried nickering again. He made a sudden scramble to get up but his legs wouldn't work right. One of his front legs gave way and the whole works went down.

He lay there flat on his side, breathing hard for a spell. His mammy nickered and kept talking to him in horse language. The spring air had a lot to do to keep Smoky from lying still very long. He gathered his legs under him to try again. Then he sniffed at the ground to make sure it was there, his head went up, his front feet stretched out in front of him. He used all the strength that was in him, and pushed himself up on his front feet. His hind legs straightened up to steady him and all he had to do was to keep his legs stiff and from folding up under him. This wasn't easy, for those long legs of his were new and doing a heap of shaking.

All would have been well maybe, only his mammy nickered "that's a good boy," and that queered Smoky. His head went up as proud as a peacock and he forgot all about keeping his legs stiff under him. Down he went and lay there the same as before.

But he didn't stay long this time. He was up again, mighty shaky, but he was up. His mammy came to him. She sniffed at him and he sniffed back. Then he nursed, and his tummy warmed up and strength came fast. Smoky was an hour and a half old and up to stay.

Things got interesting from then on, and the rest of that day was full of events for Smoky. He explored the country and at one time was as far as twelve feet away from his mammy all by himself. He shied at a rock once; it was dangerous *looking* rock and he kicked at it as he went past. That was almost too much for him and he came close to going down again. But luck was with him, and taking it all he had a mighty good time. When the sun sank over the blue ridges in the west that evening Smoky was stretched out, all tired out and fast asleep.

There wasn't a move out of him until the sun was well up and beginning to throw a good heat. His mammy nickered and that woke him. Smoky raised his head, looked around, and then began to get up. It was much easier this time and after a little while that was done. Smoky was ready for a new day.

The big day started right after Smoky had his feed. His mother moved away towards some trees a mile or so to the south. She was longing for a drink of water, but she went slowly so that little Smoky could keep up with her. There were all kinds of things he had to find out about.

A baby cottontail jumped up once right under Smoky's nose. The cottontail stood there a second, too scared to move, and pretty soon made a high dive between the colt's long legs and hit out for his hole. Smoky never saw the rabbit or he might have been running yet, because that's what he'd been looking for, an excuse to run. But at last he made up an excuse and as a long dry weed tickled his belly he let out a squeal and went from there.

His long legs tangled and untangled themselves as he ran, and he sure was making speed. Around and around he went and finally lined out straight away from where his mammy was headed. She nickered for him, and waited. He turned after a while and when he got close to his mammy he let out a buck, a squeal, a snort and stopped. He was sure some wild little horse.

It took a couple of hours for the two to make that mile to the spring. The mother drank a lot of the good water. Smoky came over and nosed at the pool, but he didn't take any of the fluid. It looked like so much thin air to him.

The rest of that day was spent around that spot. There were adventures of all kinds for Smoky. Plenty of big tree stumps gave him the scare he'd been looking for.

But there were other things more dangerous than stumps that Smoky hadn't seen. A big coyote had been watching him through dead willow branches. He wasn't at all interested in Smoky's play, only wished the colt's mammy would move away. Then he would try to get him down, for colt meat was his favorite dish.

Smoky's mammy stayed too close and the coyote finally came out of his hiding place. He squatted again, in plain sight this time. He hadn't quite made up his mind whether to go or to stick around a while longer. Just about then Smoky spotted him.

To him, the coyote was just another stump, but a stump that moved. Smoky trotted up to the coyote. The coyote just sat there and waited and when the colt got to within a few feet of him he started away just fast enough so the colt would follow. If he could only get the colt over the ridge and out of his mammy's sight!

It was all a lot of fun to Smoky, and he was bound to find out what was that gray and yellow thing that could move and didn't look at all like his mammy. It wasn't till he was over the hill that he saw all wasn't well.

The coyote had turned and, quicker than a flash, made a jump for Smoky's throat. Because his father and his grand-father and his great-grandfather had fought the wolf and the coyote, Smoky knew what to do. He whirled and let fly with both hind feet. The coyote's teeth had just pinched the skin under his jaws. But even at that, Smoky wasn't going to get rid of his enemy that easy. As he kicked he felt the weight of the coyote and then a sharp pain in his hind leg.

Smoky was scared, and he let out a squeal. It was a plain and loud enough distress signal, and it was answered. His mammy shot up the hill and took in the goings-on at a glance. Then, ears back, teeth shining, she tore up the earth and lit into the battle like a ton of dynamite.

The battle was over in a second, and, with hunks of yellow fur flying in all directions, it wound up in a chase. The coyote was in the lead and he stayed in the lead until a second hill took him out of sight.

Smoky was glad to follow his mammy back to the spring. A thin stream of blood was drying on one of his hind legs, but there was no pain. It was just a scratch. When the sun set and the shadow of his mammy spread out over him he was soon sound asleep again, and maybe dreaming of stumps, of stumps that moved.

The Spring days were great for Smoky; he found out a lot of things. He found out that grass was good to eat and water mighty fine to drink when the day was hot. He saw coyotes again, and the bigger he got the less he was afraid of 'em. Finally, he went to chasing every one of 'em he'd see.

Then one day he ran acrost another yellow animal. That animal didn't look dangerous. What's more it was hard for Smoky to make out just what it was, and he was bound to find out. He followed that animal plum to the edge of some willows. The queer part of it was that the animal didn't seem at all in a hurry to get away. It was just taking its time and Smoky was tempted to paw it. As luck would have it he didn't have the chance, the animal got in under some willows and all that was sticking out was part of its tail. Smoky took a sniff at the tail. There didn't seem to be any danger, so the next sniff he took was a little closer. That did the trick. Smoky let out a squeal and a snort as the four inch porcupine quills went into his nostrils.

But Smoky was lucky, for, if he'd been a couple of inches closer, the quills would have been rammed into his nose plum up to his eyes. As it was, there were just a few quills in his nostrils, and, compared to the real dose he might have got, it was just a warning to him. Another lesson.

It was in one of his wild scrambles down a mountain side that Smoky near run into a cinnamon bear cub which had been curled up and sleeping on the top of a big stump. Smoky stood in his tracks for a second, and in that second the cub fell off the stump with a snarl and lit a running on the other side.

Smoky went after it. Over dead timber he went, and ducked under branches. He was gaining and would of kept the chase up for quite a spell, only, just when things were getting real interesting, there was a crash and something that sounded like a landslide. In half a second more a big round head showed itself through the underbrush. Smoky saw two small eyes afire, long white teeth gleaming, and when he heard a roar that shook the mountains, Smoky left. He tore a hole in the earth as he turned tail, and raced back towards his mammy and safety.

His heart was thumping fit to burst as he got out in open country. For the life of him he couldn't figure how that little bunch of fur he'd been chasing could turn into such a cyclone. He'd never reckoned the little cub had a mammy, too.

But Smoky was learning fast. Another time on the foothills his mammy was in the lead and he was following close behind on a hot dusty trail. Of a sudden there was a rattling sound, and his mammy left the trail as though she'd been shot. Smoky did the same and none too soon. On the left, just a foot or so off the trail was a wriggling thing that had struck and missed his ankle by an inch.

Smoky stood off at a safe distance and snorted at the snake as it coiled up, ready. Somehow he had no hankering to sniff at the gray and dirty colored rattler, and when his mammy nickered for him to follow there was a warning in her nicker. He took another look at the snake. He would remember, and do the same as his mother had done whenever the rattling sound would be heard again.

The little horse was having a great time up there in that high country. He never passed anything which had him wondering for fear of missing something. If a limb cracked anywheres within hearing distance he'd perk his ears towards the sound and seldom would go on until he'd found out just why that limb cracked that way. He'd follow and pester the badger till it'd hunt a hole; he'd circle around a tree and watch the bushy-tailed squirrel as it'd climb up out of his reach. Skunks had crossed his trail, too, but somehow the atmosphere around 'em sort of made him keep his distance.

Smoky had met all the range country's wild animals excepting the lion and the wolf. His mammy kept clear of the places where these outlaws ranged. Smoky met them, too, and had scrambles with 'em but that came later in his life. It's a good thing it was later, or most likely I wouldn't be telling about Smoky now.

The first big event of Smoky's life came when he was four months old. He was standing up and asleep. His mammy was asleep too, and so were the rest of the bunch. When the cowboy that was riding up the canyon spotted them he knowed he could get above 'em and be where he could start 'em down before any of the bunch would see him.

It was a mighty good thing he done that, for, as soon as one of the bunch got wind of him, there was a snort, they came to life and were on the run. Down the side of the canyon they went, a cloud of dust and the cowboy following.

Deep and far-apart tracks were made in the steep earth as the horses slid off the mountain, jumped off ledges and

sailed acrost washouts. It was away out on the flat that Smoky
looked back and got his first sight of the human. The way
his mammy and the bunch acted made Smoky know that
here was a different kind of animal, the kind that no horse
would stop to fight but run away from, if it was possible.

But it didn't seem possible, for the rider was still right
on their tails. He stayed close till he drove the bunch into
the big log corrals. The corrals seemed to Smoky like trees
growing sideways instead of up and down. But the little
horse knowed that there was no going through them trees.
He stuck close as he could to his mammy's side. She and the
bunch milled around the big pen, the big gate closed on 'em,
and wild eyed, the bunch turned and faced a bow-legged,
leather-covered, sunburnt human.

Smoky shivered as he watched that strange creature get
off a horse just like any in the bunch excepting for a funny
hunk of leather on his back. Pretty soon the human fumbled
around a while and that hunk of leather was pulled off. The
horse shook himself and walked towards Smoky and the
bunch.

The colt never missed a thing. As soon as the loose horse
came his way he took a sniff at his sweaty hide to see just
what had been setting on him all through that long run. The

sniff left him more puzzled than ever and he looked again at the creature that was standing up on two legs.

There'd been a lot of lightning up in the mountains and Smoky had seen some fires there too. The lightning and the fires were great puzzles to the colt. So when he seen the human make a swift move with a paw, and then seen a fire in that paw, and then smoke coming out of the mouth, it made things all the harder for him to figger out. He stood and watched.

Pretty soon, the same paws that had held the fire reached down and picked up a coil of rope, a loop was made, and the human walked towards him and the bunch. At that move the bunch tore around the corral and raised the dust. Then Smoky heard the hiss of a rope as it sailed over past him and the loop settled on one of the ponies' heads. The pony was stopped and led out to the hunk of leather on the ground and it was put on him same as it'd been on the other horse. The human climbed on and that was when Smoky first set eyes on one of his kind in a fight with a two-legged creature.

It was a great sight to the colt. He watched with blazing eyes through the fight, till the pony's hard jumps dwindled down to crow-hops and then stopped. He watched the man as he got off the horse, opened the gate and led the horse out. After closing the gate he rode on and out of sight.

Then Smoky rubbed noses with his mammy and went to sniffing around the big corral. After a time he noticed a dust, and with that dust came half a dozen riders. The sight of them made Smoky hightail it to his mammy's side. Once there, he took in all that could be seen and watched the riders drive their horses through the gate and turn them in with his bunch. There was a lot of dust and milling around for there were now near two hundred horses in the big corral.

Smoky kept hid as well as he could and watched through the horses' legs. He seen on the outside, close to the pen, a fire started. Long bars of iron were passed through between the logs, with one end of them in the hot blaze. A commotion was stirred, and the bunch went to racing around the corral. Many of the horses were cut out into another corral, till there were only about fifty left, mostly colts about Smoky's age and a few quiet old mares.

Smoky had no chance to hide. He saw the bow-legged humans uncoil long ropes and heard the loops whiz past him. Terror struck in his heart and he was ready to leave the earth. It was during one of his wild scrambles for a get-away that Smoky heard the close hiss of a rope, and like a snake it coiled itself around his front legs. He let out a squeal and in another second he was flat to the ground with three feet tied up.

Smoky figgered the end of the world had come as he felt the human touch him. He cringed and quivered but he was helpless. He seen one of the creatures run towards him with a hot iron, smelled burning hair and hide. It was his own that burned, but it felt cool and there was no pain for he was at the stage where the branding iron was no worse than the touch from the human hand. But there's an end to all, whether it's good or bad, and pretty soon Smoky felt the ropes come off his legs and a boost to let him know that all was over. When he stood up and ran back to the bunch, there was a mark on his hide that was there for life, R̆ the brand read. The little horse belonged to the Rocking R outfit.

It was all a mighty great relief to Smoky and the other colts when the branding came to an end. Then the colts found their mammies and all were turned out free again, free to go back to the high mountain ranges or run on the flats.

SIXTH STORY

THE MAKINGS OF A
COWHORSE

A MONTH OR SO before the roundup wagons pull out,
the raw bronc (unbroke range horse) is enjoying a
free life with the "stock horses" (brood mares and
colts). He's coming four years old marked by the first signs
of spring. A few warm days starts him shedding, and just
as the green grass is beginning to peek out from under the
snow and living is getting easier, why, here comes a long
lanky rider on a strong grain-fed horse and hazes him and
the bunch he's with into the big corrals at the home ranch.

He's cut out with a few more of his age and put into a
small round corral—a snubbing post is in the center—and
showed where, according to the rope marks around it,
many such a bronc as him realized what they was on this
earth for.

The big corral gate squeaks open and in walks the long
lanky cowboy packing two ropes; one of them ropes sneaks
up and snares him by the front feet just when he's making
a grand rush to get away from it. He's flattened to the
ground and that other rope does the work tying him down.

A hackamore is slipped on his head while the bronc is still wondering what's happened, and from the time he's let up for a sniff at the saddle he's being eddicated, so that when the wagon pulls out a few weeks later his first promotion comes, and he's classed as "saddle stock."

From then it's 'most all up to what kind of a head that pony's got wether he'll get on further than being just a saddle horse. He may have to be pulled around a lot to get anything out of him towards what he should do, or on the other hand, he may take to it easy and get down to learning of his own accord after his bucking spells are over with.

He'll get all the time he needs to catch onto the new ropes of cow work, and only one thing at a time will be teached to him so that he'll not be rattled, but first, his bucking is what the rider'll object to and try to break him out of, and every time he bogs his head for that perticular kind of orneriness that bronc is apt to get his bellyful of the quirt.

But the cow foreman has no place on the outfit he's running for any such hombre what don't treat the ponies right, and if a cowboy is kept on the pay roll what naturally is rough on horseflesh he'll get a string of horses cut to him that's just as mean as he is and fight him right back, or even go him one better whenever the chance shows up.

There's horses though that has to be rough handled, born fighters what'll do just the opposite of what they should do to be good; they want to be ornery and them kind calls only for the real rough bronco fighter what'll fight 'em to a finish.

Them's the kind of horses what makes up a "rough string"; every cow outfit has 'em. Them horses'll range in age from five-year-old colts what craves fighting on up to fifteen- and twenty-year-old outlaws; they 'most always keep one man in the hospital steady, and when he comes out the other man is about due to take his place either with the nurses or the angels.

The good, patient "bronc twister" what takes pains to teach the bronc to be good and be a real cowhorse don't as a rule have anything to do with the "rough string"; his patience and ability with horses is too valuable to the company to have it go to waste on outlaws. So his work comes in on the uneddicated colt (the raw bronc), trying in all ways to hold the good what's in him, at the same time keeping his spirit intact, and talk him out of being ornery, if he can.

Like, for instance, that long lanky cowboy and the raw bronc I mentioned in the first part of this writing; they both have a mighty good chance of getting along fine with one another. If they do, that same bronc'll be rode out on circle and learn the ways of the critter, when later on he'll be turned over to another hand. The older cowboy, what's past hankering for "rough edges" on them broncs, will then take him and proceed to ride and help him along with his learning.

Then's when the good or the bad in him will come out to stay; at that time he knows the human enough to tell what to expect, and if he wants to be good he's got a mighty good chance, the same if he wanted to be bad, for this older hand is not hankering to get in no mix-up; the pony feels that, and *if* he's bad at heart he'll sure take advantage of it and buffalo the older cowboy to turning him loose or else buck him off in the hills somewhere.

If he succeeds in running his bluff once he'll feel sure that he can do it with every man what tries to handle him, and if he can fight wicked enough it might be hard to show him different. Consequences is, if that confidence ain't taken out of him right sudden it'll take hold on him with the result that he lands in the "rough string" and the promotion stops there

—one more what has to be tied down before he can be saddled.

But, being as I said before that this raw bronc and the long lanky cowboy had mighty good chances of getting along fine, I'll bet the good win out the same as it did with this perticular little horse I been trying to write about ever since I started this.

This little horse weighed around eleven hundred pounds and all in one hunk; what I mean is each part of him knowed what the other part was going to do and followed up according, without a kink nowheres. In bucking, or running, he'd make you wonder if he was horseflesh or dynamite. Just an ordinary horse to look at though, chunky, short back and short ankles, but with a deep chest, and that head promised a lot either way he went.

That day I run him in, throwed him, and slipped the hackamore on his head, a name for him came to me just as natural as though I'd been thinking of one for hours. "Brown Jug," and that sure fit him all the way through even to the color; also like the jug he had plenty of "kick" in him.

From the first saddling he didn't disappoint me none, for he went after me and sure made me ride; in order to stay I had to postpone fanning him for a spell and thought I was doing real well to be able to do that much. It was just my luck that none of the boys was around to see me put up such a ride on such a horse; I told 'em about it, to the way it struck me, that was mighty tame compared to how it really was, and the next day when some of them boys happened around just as I was climbing Brown Jug again, the little son of a gun just crowhopped around and acted like he loved me and my rigging 'most to death.

He bucked at every setting each day after that for about ten days; then one day as I was going through the corral gate to give him his daily "airing," he "went to pieces" right there at the gate, and where it was slick with ice he fell hard and flat on his side and smashed one of my stirrups.

Naturally the first thing came to my mind was to hold him down for a spell and see if I was caught anywheres in the rigging. I wasn't. Then I thinks that now would be a good time to teach *his kind* of a horse how bucking wasn't at all nice, so I proceeds to tie him down. That don't hurt a horse, only his feelings, specially so when interrupted that way in the middle of the performance.

I'd whipped him some while bucking a few days before and I found out before I was through that his kind had to be handled different, 'cause he bucked and showed fight all the way through and never let up till he was tired out, then he went to sulking. After that I watched my chance for some other way to break him out of it.

My chance came when he fell and I didn't let it slip by. I gave him a good half hour to think it over, and when I let him up, me a-setting in the saddle, he was glad to get away from the forced rest and be able to stand on his pins again; but he was sure took down a peg, and when I loped him out sudden he seemed to've forgot that was the time he liked to buck best.

There was twelve broncs in my string, each was getting short rides on "inside circle," or at the cutting grounds. Their teaching came right along with the cattle and the average of them colts was coming fine, but Brown Jug was ahead of 'em all and naturally I helped him all the more.

He'd bucked only once since I tied him down and that second time he didn't get to buck like he wanted to then; he'd only made a half a dozen jumps, when I reached down on one rein, pulled his head up and jerked his feet out from

under him, laying him down again just when he wanted to
be in action the most.

That fixed him for good, and I figgered if he'd ever buck
again it'd be when he got cold and wanted to warm up, or
when somebody'd tickle him with the spur at the wrong
time. Well, if he did it'd only show he had feelings and the
kind of spirit that makes the cowhorse.

It was a couple of weeks since Brown Jug'd bucked last;
it was out of his system by now and I was beginning to take
a lot of interest in the ways of handling the critter. I kept
him in my string long as I could; then one day the foreman, who'd been watching with an eagle eye the work of
every colt I'd been breaking, figgered the "raw edge" was
pretty well took off them broncs and fit to be divided up
amongst the boys for easy work.

The next morning I'm ready to leave the wagon behind,
also the ponies I'd broke, and hit back for the home ranch
on a gentle horse, where I'm to round up another string of

raw broncs and start in breaking fresh. But before leaving I manages to get the foreman to one side. "Now, Tom," I says, "there's one special little horse in them broncs I'm turning over what has the makings of a 'top horse' and I'd sure like to see a real good man get him, a man that'll make him what he promises to be. I know Flint Andrews would sure like to have him, and I'm asking as a favor if you'd see that Flint gets Brown Jug."

"You surprise me, Bill," he says, squinting over Brown Jug's way, then back at me, "why, I thought all horses was alike to you no matter how good or bad they be; but I guess I thought wrong, and if you'd like to see Flint get the brown horse don't worry about it, he'll get him."

"That's the trouble being a bronc peeler and working for them big cow outfits," I says to my horse as I'm riding along back to the ranch; "a feller don't no more than begin to get interested in the way the colts are learning; and just about the time the orneriness is took out of 'em and they're behaving fine they're took away and scattered along in the other boys' strings, and another bunch of green, raw, fighting broncs takes their place."

I'm at the ranch near three weeks and coming along pretty fair with the new bunch when the wagons begin pulling in. The spring roundup was over with, and three of the four remudas was being corralled one after another; cow-horses, night horses, and circle horses was being cut out and turned on the range to rest up till the next spring, over five hundred head of 'em, and the other two hundred was put in the pasture to keep going till fall roundup. Them was the colts what'd just been "started" that spring along with the "spoiled horses" what belonged most to the "rough string," and needed steady setting on in order to make 'em good.

Brown Jug came in with one of the remudas and was looking fine, Flint couldn't get to me quick enough to tell me what a great little horse he was, and how near he could come to being human. "Never kettled [bucked] once," he says, "and I never saw a horse getting so much fun out of beating a critter at her own game as he does; he sure camps on their hocks from start to finish."

A few days later I had a chance to watch him at work. Flint was a-talking away to him and that little son of a gun of a horse seemed to understand everything he said and talk right back with them ears and eyes of his. I was getting jealous of what Flint could do with Brown Jug, and it set me down a peg to see that he sure had me beat in teaching him something. I was all right when it come to starting a colt and taking the rough off him, but after that I sure had to take a back seat from Flint.

The boys was rounding up fresh horses and the wagons was getting ready to pull out again, all the corrals was being used and every rider was topping off the horses cut to him; from ten to fifteen head of the big fat geldings is what made a "string," and the company saw that each cowboy had all he needed far as horseflesh was concerned.

And when the four- and six-horse teams was hooked on the "chuck," "bed," and "wood" wagons and the big corral gates was opened to let the remuda follow, every cowboy was on hand and ready. "The pilot" (rider piloting the wagon through the roadless plains and breaks) started, the cook straightened out his team and followed with the chuck wagon, then the "flunky" next with the bed wagon, and the "nighthawk" (night herder for the saddle horses) on the wood wagon took up the swing, then last came the day wrangler bringing up the rear with upward of two hundred head of saddle stock, the remuda.

Fifteen or more of us riders rode along the side, doing nothing in perticular but keeping our ponies right side up till we come to the country where the work begins. The whole outfit moved on a fast trot and sometimes going down a sag you could see the cook letting his team hit out on a high lope, and the rest was more than aching to keep up.

Two more such outfits was to start out soon for other directions and on other ranges. I went along with the first; the broncs I'd just started a few weeks before was in the remuda and on the trail of eddication to the ways of the critter, the same as the bunch I'd took along early that spring.

In this new string of broncs I was putting through the ropes, there was another special little horse what promised to come up along with Brown Jug as a cowhorse. But I was kinda worried, he was *too* good, never bucked once and seemed to try too hard to learn. His kind of a horse was hard for me to make out, 'cause they was few. I always felt they was waiting for a chance to get you, and get you good whenever that chance showed up.

I figgered a horse with a good working set of brains like he had ought to've done *something*, but all he did do was to watch me like a hawk in every move I'd make; and he was so quiet when I was around that I naturally felt kind of nervous, thinking he might explode and tear up the scenery 'most any minute.

But he stayed good and kept a-learning fast, and even though I figgered he might be one example of a horse in a thousand, I was still dubious when I turned him and a few others of my broncs over to the boys. I wished he'd bucked, once anyway.

I kept my eye on him, and every time it was his turn to
be rode I was always surprised to see how docile he was.
The new hand what was riding him made an awful fuss over
"Sundown," as he'd called him (he was too much of a puzzle
for *me* to name) and the two was getting along better than
I ever expected.

With Brown Jug, he was showing a little orneriness now
and again, but that was to be expected, and Flint could 'most
always talk him out of it. He done the work though, and
was getting so he could turn a "bunch-quitting" critter so
fast she'd think she was born that way.

And, if you'd asked me right quick which one of them
two ponies, Brown Jug or Sundown, would make the best
cowhorse I'd said Brown Jug; on the other hand, if you'd let
me think it over for a spell it'd been that to my way of thinking the two horses don't compare; they're both working fine,
but I trust Brown Jug and I can't as yet trust Sundown. Anyway, to put myself in the clear I'd said, "let's wait and see."

My broncs being all took away but four, a string of "cut,"
"circle," and "night" horses are turned over to me and I
gets in on circle day herd and night guard with the rest of
the boys, so now I can watch the colts I'd started get their
finished eddication.

Fall was coming on and the air was getting crimpy; the
light frosts was turning the grass to brown, and the old
ponies was developing a hump in their backs and had to
have their bucking space to warm up in before straightening
out and tending to business.

For the good old honest hard-working cowhorse does
buck, and buck mighty hard sometimes, specially on cold
mornings, but he's never "scratched" for it. The cowboy
a-setting atop of him will only grin at the perticular way the

pony has of unlimbering for the work what's ahead of him on the "cutting grounds." He'll be talked to a lot and kidded along for his "crooked ways," while he's tearing up the earth and trying to be serious in his bucking, and never will either the quirt or the spur touch that pony's hide while he's acting on that way, for him being a cowhorse and at the top of the ladder in saddle stock gives him a lot of privilege.

The cowhorse I'm speaking of here is the *real one*, the same you'd find anywheres, some years ago, even today on the big cow outfits to the east of the Rockies and on the plateaus stretching from Mexico to Canada. This cowhorse done nothing but cow work where it'd need a pony of his kind. He never was rode out on circle or straight riding and never was used anywheres outside of on the cutting grounds. All the action, strength, endurance, and intelligence that pony has was called for *there*, and the horse that could do that work and do it well was worth near his weight in gold to the country.

I well remember the time, and not so long ago, when you could buy any amount of mighty good saddle horses for from five to twenty dollars a head, well-reined horses that could turn a Sonora "yak" quicker than you could wink; and I'll leave it to any cowman what savvies them cattle that that's saying a lot. But there was something them same ponies lacked to make 'em real cowhorses; what they lacked was intelligence, knowing where to be ahead of time when the snaky critter side-winded here or there, and put 'er out of the "main herd" before she had time to double back. Them same ponies depended too much on the touch of the rein; they couldn't see themselves what they should do, and far as they'd get in saddle stock was "day herd," "circle," or "rope horse."

Where with the real cowhorse, he's the kind what'll work *with* the man, he's got to be able to see what should be done man only shows him the work and coaches him along some, times things are done so quick in working a herd or cutting out a critter that the human eye or hand may be too slow, and that's where the instinct of the cowhorse comes in, to pick up the slack. He's got brains enough to know what the cowboy wants done, and he goes ahead and does it.

Man is not all responsible for making the cowhorse what he is; you got to give the pony half the credit, for after all, man only shows him the work and coaches him along some, but the horse himself does that work and will take enough interest in it as to sometimes bite a hunk of rawhide and beef right off some critter's rump if that critter happens to act ornery.

You can see feelings and wisdom all over that pony as he winds in and out through the herd. He goes along with his head straight from the body, not paying no attention to any of the bellering herd around him. The cowboy leaves the reins hanging loose and then, of a sudden, the horse is given a sign which is really *no sign at all*, but anyway the pony knows *somehow* that the rider has a critter located and to be cut out; and even though there may be some cattle between him and that certain critter, he has a strong hunch just which one it is; that's enough for the cowhorse to work on.

Such a horse couldn't be bought at all, and many a time I've seen two hundred dollars or more (that was a lot of money then) offered and turned down for the likes, when the other well-reined kind could be got in trade, for only a saddle blanket or a box of cartridges. Yes, sir, you'd had to buy the whole kaboodle, cattle, horses, range, and all, in order to get the cowhorse I'm speaking of here.

And Brown Jug, he was turning out to be just that kind of a horse. That fall after his first summer of eddication with the cow, he showed strong where in a couple more years he'd be a top cowhorse, the kind what's talked about around the cow camps from the Rio Grande to the Yellowstone. Flint was always raving about him and I'd always chip in with "well, look who started him."

Sundown was coming up right along with Brown Jug, and the new hand what was riding him sure used to get into some long sizzling arguments with Flint over them two ponies, but the argument kept neck to neck, same as it did with the horses.

They was both turned out that fall together with the rest of the remuda. That winter was easy on all stock, and the horses was all packing a big fat when spring broke up.

The spring horse roundup brought in near a thousand head of saddle stock, and in one of the corrals with other horses I got first glimpse of Brown Jug and Sundown. They'd been pals all winter and where one went the other followed; if one got into a scrap the other helped him and they sure made a dandy pair.

Flint'd been complaining of getting old and stiff for a week or so past, and when he seen Brown Jug acting snorty he mentioned it again, and a little stronger this time. Finally I took the hint and told him I'd top him off for him if he wanted me to. "Sure," he says, "I don't mind."

Well, sir, that little horse gave me a shaking up the likes I never had before or since, and when he finally quit and I got off, I was beginning to feel old and stiff myself, but I rode him again that afternoon and took it out of him easy enough. The next day he was all right and Flint rode him away.

In another corral something was more than raising the dust, and soon as I see what causes it, I don't lose no time to climb the poles and get there. Sundown had "broke in two" *at last*. The new hand was having it out with him but he had no chance. Somehow he stayed on though and when the horse quit he fell off like a rag.

I takes a turn at that horse and tired as he is he sure makes it interesting, and I don't find no time to use the quirt. He finally quits again and I was mighty glad of it. He's standing with legs wide apart, fire in his eyes and puffing away like a steam engine and when I tries to move him out of his tracks, all I gets is a couple more hard stiff jolts. He's mad clear through and I know there's no use trying to make him do anything just then.

From then on he was just as bad this spring as he was good the spring before. All that could be got of him was buck, fight, sulk, and stampede. He was no more interested in anything else, and after he put a couple of boys in the hospital and come darn near getting me, he was put in the "rough string."

I wasn't surprised to see him turn out that way; if anything, I kind of expected it. For even though I've seen a *few* what never bucked on first setting and stayed good all the time, I always figgered there was something wrong with 'em and could never trust 'em till I knowed for sure.

I quit the outfit that year, right after the spring roundup was over, and it was a couple of years later when I rode back into that country. The spring roundup was in full swing and a herd was being "worked" a little ways from camp.

I rides over, and there was Flint and Brown Jug working *together,* and doing the prettiest job of cutting out I ever saw. A long-legged and long-horned staggy-looking critter was being edged to the outside of the herd, and I could see that critter had no intentions of being put out of that herd, none at all.

Pretty soon an opening shows up, and Brown Jug come pretty near seeing it quicker than Flint. Anyway that critter was stepped on from there and put out before she knowed it. She tries to turn back, but the little horse was right on hand at each sidestep, when of a sudden Brown Jug stumbles. His foot had gone down a badger hole and he come near turning over. Flint quits him, and when the little horse straightens up the bridle is off his head. All was done quicker than you could think and the critter hadn't had time to get back to the herd.

Then Brown Jug sees 'er and, transformed into a lightning streak, he lands on 'er; the fur is flying off that critter's rump and that little horse without man or bridle keeps on

as though nothing happened and puts 'er out of the herd and heads 'er for the cut.

Nobody says anything for a spell, but the expressions means a lot. Then the foreman, who'd seen it all, kinda grins and says: "If I had a few more horses like that I wouldn't need no men."

A few days later that same foreman piles his rope on Brown Jug, leads him out, and puts his own saddle on him. That sure set me to thinking, for even the boss is not supposed to ride any horse the company furnishes you with in your string, and still wondering I looks over at Flint, who's leading out the boss's top horse and putting *his* saddle on him.

I finds out afterwards that they'd swapped, and that Flint was to get his wages raised to boot, but I could see that Flint wasn't any too happy over the trade and I says to him: "I guess you feel about the same now as I did when *I had* to turn him over to you three years ago."

"Yes," he answers, "and worse."

But even at that, we was both mighty proud that we'd helped make Brown Jug what he was, *the top cowhorse of four remudas.*

CHAPO – THE FAKER

F EW SADDLE HORSES are the size Chapo was. The name Chapo didn't at all fit him and maybe that was why he was called such. For Chapo is Spanish for a small, chunky horse and this Chapo was everything but that. He wasn't only tall but broad and weighed close to thirteen hundred pounds, the weight of a good size draft horse. But he carried that weight mighty well, was proportioned and built about perfect, and he had the quick fast action of a nine-hundred-pound cowhorse.

Mighty few saddle horses of his size are much good for fast and hard range work. Such horses are used mostly for corral work, snubbing or heavy roping, or "riding bog" (pulling out bogged down cattle). But when such a size horse is a good one, meaning in action and what all the smaller horse is, he's usually a *very* good one, as good as he's rare.

Chapo was one of that rare kind. With all his size he was active as a cat. He was very much that way when I come to work for the outfit he belonged to and was turned in my string. But he was of no more use by then, even tho he was still of good age, fat as a seal and had never been hurt.

He'd turned tricky, and fact was, as the foreman frankly told me, he hadn't been rode for a couple of years on that account. That was all the foreman told me about the horse, which is considerable more than a cowboy is usually told about any horse when he hires out to any outfit. If he's told, especially by the other riders, he won't listen, for he's apt to be told just the opposite of how this or that horse might act. That's done partly in a joking way but more to test the newcomer as to his experience—if he's a top hand, medium or of no account, if he's rode far and wide, is a home guard or just green.

That's usually guessed pretty close soon as the new hand catches the first horse in his string. A string ranges from six to sometimes as many as fourteen head of different kinds of horses for different uses, to each rider, and the cowboy who's rode far and wide, for big outfits and is a good hand doesn't ask about any horse in the string that's turned over to him, nor listens to what he might be told about 'em. With his experience in handling more than many and all kinds of horses, he practically can tell the caliber of most any horse by a glance of him and the second his loop tightens around that horse's neck. If not then, he'll usually find out at the first sitting.

But some horses, not going the humans one better, don't show their true caliber until some particular thing happens. That might not show up until after a dozen rides, and when you might get to think you know and can trust him, he'll bust wide open with all the meanness that's really in him, catch you napping (unawares) and get you, all depends on your sense of riding and general knowing of horses.

It would of been as well for me, or maybe better, if that foreman had told me about Chapo being tricky. I didn't ask him in which way, but just the looks, actions and great size of that horse was enough to warn any cowboy who dabbed his rope on him.

He stopped sudden, turned and faced me quick as my loop settled over his head, and holding it high he followed my lead, snorting, out of the bunch. Well, I figured right there, he sure wasn't a jerk-away anyhow, and that was one fine point, especially when a rider is off his horse and many miles away from camp.

With his head held high the way he did, he looked as tall as a giraffe and my five feet eleven more like that of a pigmy. But for a horse that hadn't been rode for a couple of years, and fat and good feeling as he was, I didn't think he was so bad, just acting natural. It was also natural when he struck at me a couple of times as I come up the rope to within touching distance of his nose. I was expecting that, and to put an end to such action I flipped the end of my rope around his front feet. I seen then too, the way he just stood and trembled, that that had been done to him plenty times before and well busted (thrown) when he run against it.

Watching his hind hoofs, which might reach up quicker than I could see, I then put my twisted rawhide hobbles on his front ones. The next was to slip my hackamore on his sky-high head, and there's where I had the beginning of some trouble, for he was mighty head-shy and would hardly let me touch it. But by going easy I managed to work a half hitch over his nose and I could then touch him up to his eyes. I got the hackamore that far, and there I was stuck, for he held his head not only near out of my reach but jerked it as I'd try to get the hackamore headstall over his eye and close to his ears, and as he'd jerk that way he'd rear and strike with both hobbled front feet. But I'd be close to his shoulder at such times and the flying hoofs would graze past.

I seen then, as I tried to ease the hackamore headstall over his eyes on up, that he had a "bug in his ear." Sometimes such head and ear shyness *is* caused by a bug, maybe a wood tick that gets in the ear and makes a sore. But with Chapo I could see it was only plain fear of being eared down, which I found out afterwards had often been done so'd he wouldn't kick the rider while getting on or off of him.

After his two years of freedom he was of course much touchier about that left ear of his, and no matter how easy and careful I tried, I couldn't get my hackamore above his eye. But I'd had dealings with such horses before, so, instead of trying to slip the hackamore from the front and over his eyes up to his ears, I unfastened the headstall, slipped it around his neck to the back of his ears, where I wanted it, and fastened it there. He didn't seem to mind that so much, and being that on a horse broke to the bit I also used a bridle over the hackamore, I slipped it on his head in the same way.

Bridling was about the worst about him while handling him from the ground, and by easy stages I gradually broke him of that, for I didn't twist his ear to get on or off of him, even tho at different times I come near having to do it.

He wasn't so bad to saddle, not if he was hobbled and you didn't jab him in any way the while. When such happened he could bring up a hind hoof and kick well ahead of his shoulder point, from a standstill and even tho hobbled. As I've already said he was active and limber as a cat.

I figured I was sure due for a tough ride the first time I prepared to get on him. It's always best to expect the worst and be ready, but what I was leary of the most was them far-reaching hind hoofs of his as I'd go to get on, that would be one of his tricks.

Without taking the hobbles off and standing well by and ahead of his shoulder, I took a hold of the "bosal" (hacka-more nose band) and bridle cheek with my left hand. Chapo stood a-quiver at that, like ready and expecting me to reach for the stirrup. I felt that, and so, instead of reaching for the stirrup with my right hand, I reached for the saddle horn, wiggled the saddle some to make sure it was on tight enough to stay, and then, to the tense horse's surprise, I of a sudden doubled up with both knees to land high on his shoulder, to ride alongside there and just ahead of the saddle.

Well. . . . That horse like to've had a cat fit at that trick, which I seen right away had never been tried on him before. I was too high for him to reach with a hoof, and as he went up in a wide-winding buck-jump, being hobbled and out of kilter, he near doubled up on his neck instead of landing on his feet as he came down, and I, being free, easy cleared his fall.

I was again on his shoulder before he got entirely to his feet but he didn't do much high flying jumps any more after that, just circled sideways some and tried to whirl me off. . . . When he finally come to a standstill and while all a-puzzled, I slid down to the ground, took off the hobbles and then eased into the saddle without him hardly seeming to realize. Anyhow he didn't make a move.

And when I did move him, and sort of made him come to with a light pop of my quirt, it was my turn to be sur-prised, for instead of lighting into the powerful and hard bucking as his actions all indicated he was sure aching to do, he just went to crowhopping, then to bucking, but not hard enough to throw even a stool-riding drugstore cowboy off.

I must of looked my surprise, for a few of the riders that was near had to laugh, and I was then told that that was about the worst bucking he ever done.

I rode Chapo when his turn come, every two or three days, and thought he was a good circle horse (for roundup rides). The tricks I'd so far found in him wasn't any worse than could be expected from most circle horses, for them are horses that can't very well be used as cowhorses. They're usually the kind that take no interest in the ways of handling stock, and it's up to the cowboy riding 'em to put 'em to work in covering the country, rounding up and driving whatever stock is found to gather all in one herd at the "cutting grounds" (where what stock is wanted is held and the not wanted cut out; that's cowhorse work).

The circle horse string is usually made up of mature colts, cold-jawed and spoilt horses. Tough ones, and it don't matter so much if they can't be turned on a dime, as the good cowhorse can do, so long as they can stand a good ride at good speed, and can be turned to within a hundred yards more or less while chasing and rounding up stock.

After riding Chapo for about a month, whenever his turn come, I got to figure that the worst of his tricks was when I handled him from the ground. I finally cured him of them pretty well, but according to what the foreman had told me of him I kept a-thinking there sure must of been more and worse tricks than the ones I'd found to make the foreman pass that remark and warning. I had other and worse horses in my string than Chapo was and nothing was said of them. So I kept a-thinking there must be some other and still worse tricks in him which hadn't as yet come to the top or he sure wouldn't been left to run loose for two whole years.

Not on account of what few tricks I had discovered in him.

I wouldn't of course ask the foreman as to what trick or tricks he meant Chapo had, for, as range etiquette points out, it's not the proper thing to do. So, as I'd be riding him once in a while I'd be wondering, and sort of curious as to what hidden tricks Chapo might have deep in him, which he'd be apt to bust out with most any time. That made me keep alert and sort of tense and ready for when one would pop, and that's where I felt it would of been better if the foreman hadn't warned me of Chapo's trickiness. I figured I could of been a match to any of 'em.

But as it was, always on the watch out as I rode him, he sometimes got me to do some scary wondering. Like for instance, when riding him on the top or steep side of a high peak that horse seemed to sense that I was anything but bold and brave when up so high in such places. Maybe he felt it by the way I hugged my saddle so tight and was so much nicer to him away up there.

There come one especial time, while I was riding him amongst steep pinnacles, high razor-back ridges and narrow ledges, when that horse kept a-spooking and gave me about all the scares I could stand for a spell. This was in a badland strip of country, deep ravines and near bottomless holes. But there was some pretty fair feed took hold in crags and amongst the little brush in some places. The wilder cattle would hit for such country during roundup time and hide away in there. Consequences was, that rough country had to be rode much closer than the more open.

I think I rode my saddle closer when I did the country that time, for Chapo seemed to enjoy scaring the life out of me by acting up at the most dangerous places, like spooking at his own tail, even saddle strings, and other things he wouldn't spook at any other time. He'd then hump up, jump around some and like he would go into a bucking or stampeding fit, right in such places where even a mountain goat would be careful of every step and the missing of one would mean a downward trip to China.

I somehow managed to live thru the scares, combed my scope of what cattle there was in it, and them being plenty fat and wild they didn't need chasing when once found out. They just left that country at the sight of me and as tho it was haunted, and the echo of my holler, when I wasn't too scared to, worked as if spooks was on their tails.

My circle done and finally getting out of the badlands to catch up with what cattle I'd scared out and thrown with more bunches other riders had got out, the scares that Chapo horse had given me begin to sort of react on me, against him, for now that the most dangerous places was past he was as well behaving and willing as he'd been spooky, ornery and stubborn before.

That made me peeved to the point where, as I thought on his scary tricks, I finally got good and mad at him and decided to take all the orneriness out of him right there and then, also whatever other streaks of trickiness he might have away deep in him. I was seeing red, but I gave him his head so he'd be free to bring on all the action he wanted and all to his heart's content as I hooked him in the shoulder and unlimbered my quirt on him.

The first jump he made liked to broke my back. But I'd asked for that battle, and at it we went. I'm sure that, according to what the boys had told me, that Chapo bucked very much harder then than he ever had before. He done a sure enough powerful job of it and I wished some of the boys had been near to see for I knew they'd agree with me.

I was high and wide from my saddle quite a few times during the battle, and I wasn't mad no more now as I kept dragging my quirt on him all I could, I was just determined, determined to whip all that orneriness out of him and whatever more he'd been storing, and to win that battle, I had to.

And I did, even if it was nip and tuck a few times. . . . When he finally throwed his head up and broke into a crowhopping run I was glad of it, for I'd had about enough too.

It was a couple of days later when it again come his turn to be rode, seldom over half a day to the turn, for we changed to fresh horses three times a day. He was snorty as ever before when I caught him, like he'd forgot all about the battle we'd had and of his losing it.

I knew his caliber and that what ornery streak was in him could never be taken out. He'd have that in him for as long as he lived and was able to navigate. But what still stumped me was what trick or tricks was it that the foreman remarked of that horse having. It sure must be odd and special ones, and which hadn't showed up as yet. I'd sure given him all the chances and encouragement to bring out all the bad that was in him, and even tho he'd turned on most every trick and twist a horse could the last time I'd rode him, there'd been nothing much out of the ordinary from what all a good tough and ornery horse would do. So, by that and the foreman's remark I figured there must be still more to come.

Thru curiosity I come near asking him, but again thinking the better of it I decided to forget about it and take that horse as he come. Him and me had only that one battle and after that we got along well, as well as could be expected.

Then, a short time afterwards, when it was again his turn to be rode I noticed as I caught him that there was a sort of halfway meek look in his usually watchful and challeng-

WILL JAMES
III—

ing eye. He was also some easier to bridle and saddle. I got on him without feeling I had to watch for a hind hoof, and when I started him out for that morning's ride he went along like a good one.

Even the other riders noticed that difference in him, and there was grinning remarks such as, "Maybe he ain't feeling well," or, "I guess it's a change of heart," and so on passed around.

The last remark, the one about a change of heart kind of stuck to me. Maybe, I thought, the ornery son of a wolf did decide to change to the good, maybe a long pondered on conclusion from the good battle we had. Then, I thought again, or was it that he'd pondered on the other trick or tricks of his which the foreman had remarked about. . . . Maybe he was scheming on that now, to catch me napping.

But he wouldn't catch me napping, I figured, or getting too careless. . . . Nothing happened, only, when just a few miles from camp, I thought I felt him favoring his left front leg. A ways further on I was sure of a limp in that leg, and then, a couple of miles more and that horse was sure enough lame. . . . Too lame to go on and it would be plenty hard enough to get him back to camp, I thought, so as to unsaddle and turn him loose.

That lameness all come on him before we got to a point where the foreman would scatter us riders to different points, to circle and comb the country of what stock was there, driving all to the roundup grounds, near camp.

As we rode along, I noticed the foreman looking at my limping horse and sort of grinning to himself. I wondered about that, also that he didn't seem at all concerned about the horse's lameness. But I was, and was about to tell him I'd be turning back when he beat me to it, and grinning some more, he just said, "All right, Bill. We'll see you in camp at noon."

It then came to me as I turned Chapo back for camp that there was something queer about his kind of sudden lameness, without a run, twist or jump to cause it. Then the foreman's knowing grin. . . .

It came to me all the plainer as, a ways after I'd turned the horse towards camp, he begin to lose his lameness, until before I got there it was practically gone. I knew then what was up. That wise Chapo had faked that lameness, and when he was again turned loose with the remuda (saddle bunch) there wasn't a sign of a limp in him.

I'd had horses fake in different ways with me before, but none had acted the part quite as well as Chapo had, and another thing, whether Chapo had been faking or not there's sure no pleasure in riding a lame horse. There was many others, and mighty, mighty few ever fake.

That noon, during the change of horses and as I caught another horse, the foreman told me that now Chapo would play lame for some time, maybe until roundup was over, then hide out on some other range when time for the next roundup come.

He was a wise one. If he couldn't outdo his rider, and one got the better of him after all his tricks had played out, he'd always fall back on the one trick such as the one he'd played on me and finally won. That was his hole card and the trick I'd wondered about. Fake lameness.

EIGHTH STORY

A NARROW ESCAPE

I WAS RIDING ALONG one day whistling a tune, my horse was behaving fine and all was hunkydory and peaceful. Ahead a ways I'd noticed a narrow washout and I kept on a riding. I'd rode over many a one of them, and nothing was there to warn me that I should go around this perticular one.

My horse cleared the opening and I was still a whistling, then, of a sudden my whistling stopped short as I felt the earth go out from under my horse's feet, . . . the next thing I know I was in the bottom of a ten-foot washout and underneath twelve hundred pounds of horseflesh.

I was pinned there to stay, and lucky I thought afterward that my whole body wasn't underneath that horse. It could of just as well been that way, only past experiences with horses had saved me and natural instinct had made me try to stay on top of the horse whether he was upside down or right side up. As it was, I was kind of on the side of him, my head was along his neck and only my left hip and leg felt the pinch of the weight.

The washout was only about three feet wide, at the bottom, just enough room for me and that horse to get wedged in nice. The old pony was fighting and bellering and kicking big hunks of dirt down on top of us. I was kinda worried that he might undermine the bank of the washout and have it cave in on us and bury us alive so I grabbed his head and hugged it toward me thinking that would quiet him down and keep him from tearing things up so much. I figgered that if there'd be any squeezing done it would be on the other side, for as it was I sure had no room to spare.

Well, he fought on for quite a spell, then he laid still for a while. If that horse had been good and gentle I could of maybe got him to lay still long enough so I could try and dig myself out with my hands, but just as soon as I'd move to try anything like that he'd let out a snort that sounded mighty loud in that perticular place and go to fighting again.

His hoofs would start flying and tearing things up and what little dirt I'd scraped away with my fingers would be replaced with a few hundred pounds of the side of the washout. I was having a mighty hard time keeping my head clear and out in the air and the dirt kept accumulating and piling up on top of us till there was nothing but part of the horse's legs, still a going, and our heads sticking out.

Then it comes to me that if that horse keeps on a kicking and bringing down more dirt he'd soon be in a fix where his legs would be all buried and he'd have to be still, but I was sure worried about a big hunk of overhanging dirt he might loosen up while doing that. It looked like it weighed at least five tons and I didn't want to think of it dropping down on us.

There was one way where I could win out, and that was to dig for my six-shooter which it was lucky was on my right hip and possible to get at. With that six-gun I could shoot the horse, there'd be no more dirt coming down and I could easy enough dig myself out with the same gun, and I could take my time about it too.

That was one way and the best one, but I sure didn't want to shoot that horse and decided I wouldn't till I just had to to save him from suffering. Shooting a horse wasn't appealing to me even in the fix I was in. It would of saved my carcass for sure but I was finding more pleasure in looking for other ways out than just that one.

I kept my eye on the hunk of dirt above my head, and while the pony by me would have another fit once in a while and small piles of dirt would keep a coming down I was finding my breathing capacity getting smaller and smaller. My body was beginning to feel numb from my chest on down and I felt that the only part of me that was living was from my chest on up.

I thought of the boys I started out from camp with that morning and wondered *when* they'd miss me and start looking for me, and then once again I thought of my six-gun. If I could get it out and fire a shot once in a while some of 'em would maybe hear.

I'd been digging pretty steady and with just the idea of keeping my right arm and head clear. I knowed that I couldn't get away even if all the dirt was off—the horse was on me and holding me down, but from then on I wanted my gun and I sure went to work for it.

It took me a good hour's time to get it out and my gloves was wore to a frazzle, but I finally managed it, and soon as I shook the dirt out of the barrel I held it straight up and fired. The shot echoed along the washout and sounded like it could be heard for many miles. I waited and listened for an answer and then I noticed where the sun was. It was slanting in where me and my pony was getting buried alive and it was making things all the hotter down there.

By it I figgered it was along about noon, all the boys excepting me would be back to camp from the first "circle" and wouldn't be starting out again for a while. I was about ten miles from camp and when they would start out again I knowed they'd go another direction as all the cattle in the country I was at was run in that morning. The shot I fired had been for nothing.

Riders was often late getting in with cattle and I knowed they hadn't thought anything had happened to me as yet. I also knowed they wouldn't think anything was wrong till that evening when they gathered in to eat, and till then I thought was an ungodly long time to wait.

And what was more, how was they going to find me if they did start looking. I was sure well hid and they'd have to pretty near know the exact spot where I was located, I could make a noise with my gun of course. . . . All them thoughts was mighty cheerful thoughts not to have, but I couldn't dodge 'em. If only that big ton of dirt above my head hadn't been so threatening things would of been easier, but there it was as big as death and I couldn't take my eyes from it.

Finally the sun left us. It was going on west to its setting point and left me still doing some some tall thinking. The big horse alongside of me was quiet for good—the dirt had piled up on top of him till his toes disappeared and he *had* to be still. But his breathing wasn't very good to listen to so close to my head, and I didn't find it at all inspiring as to ways and means of getting out of there.

Clods of dirt would still keep a falling off and on but there was signs of 'em quitting since the horse had got quiet.

It was too late for me to try to dig out though, but I was still at it and at the same time watching that I didn't tickle or jar the side of the bank that held the all-powerful heavy piece of earth.

As I worked and clawed at the dirt and wished for badger claws instead of bleeding fingers I found that my resting spells was coming oftener and stayed longer. It was just as the sun was going down and when I'd took an *unusual* long rest that I realized I was holding something in my hand that I'd grabbed a hold of when I was ready to quit. It was a clump of rabbit brush that'd fell in from the top with the dirt that'd got loosened—more of it was a hanging up there.

My hand was on my chest as I studied where that piece of brush had come from. I felt a chill run up and down my backbone as I realized that it'd come from no other place than the big hunk of overhanging dirt. *It was loosening up.*

The thought of that near had me moving, my hand closed in on my shirt just for something to grab a hold of, and as I did that I felt something breaking in my shirt pocket. It was matches.

I held my hand there for a while and done some thinking. I noticed the clump of rabbit brush my hand was still holding and then I looked up ten feet above to where there was lots of the same brush hanging over the edge.

I couldn't think so very fast along about then and I only realized it was dark when I lit a match and it throwed a light, but the rest of the programme didn't need no thinking —everything was in front of me to follow and that's what I did.

I held the match under the piece of rabbit brush I had and it took holt and flamed like that kind of brush does. When I thought the flame was strong enough to stand a little breeze I heaved it as best I could up toward the other brush ten feet above me.

The first attempt wasn't much good, the little piece of brush came back on me, singed me a little and then died. I tried it again and finally landed it up amongst the brush along the top of the bank. Then I held my breath.

A little flame shot up and throwed a light on the opposite side of the washout. I watched that and seen where the flame seemed to gradually die down. "If that fire don't start," I says out loud, "I'm just as good as done for," which was the truth.

But it did start, slow and aggravating but sure, and pretty soon it gets lit up above, and I can see the sparks fly and some of 'em are falling down on me and the horse but it was sure good to see that light and hear that brush a roaring in flame. I knowed what rabbit brush would do once it got started to burning. I knowed it'd spread and throw a mighty good light for as long as any of that kind of brush was around. And if I remembered right, that kind of brush was plenty thick along that wash for a good mile or so.

From then on instead of digging I put my efforts to waiting and that was getting to be some painful too, but my hopes had went up a lot since I got such a good signal fire started. I felt sure somebody would ride up and look for me soon, and sure enough, after a while I hear somebody holler, my six-shooter barks out an answer and then I thinks, . . . what if somebody should ride upon that piece of country that's hanging over me and just waiting for some little weight to start it down.

The thought of that sure got my lungs to working. . . . "Stay back," I hollered, "stay back."

"Where are you, Bill?" somebody asks.

"In the bottom of the washout," I answers, "but don't come near the edge of where I'm at or it'll cave in—get in from some other place."

I didn't have to tell them to hurry, they was doing that a plenty and pretty soon half a dozen riders was digging me out with running irons, six-shooters, and everything they could get hold of that'd scatter the dirt. The horse was lifted off of me and I was pulled out to where I could work my legs and get the blood to circulating in 'em.

It took four saddle horses to pull my horse out and straighten him up to stand, and by the time I got through telling the boys what happened, how it happened and all I felt half-ways strong enough to stand up again. With the help of one of the boys I walked over to investigate the hunk of earth that'd been hanging over me and threatening all that long day. There was a crack in the ground and back of it which showed how ready it was to fall. I stuck my boot heel in that crack and shoved a little, and about that time I was pulled away.

The earth seemed to go out from under us as that hunk left, a big cloud of dust went up, and when we looked again the washout was near filled to the top.

NINTH STORY

WHEN IN ROME –

T HINGS ARE SURE a-popping now, cowboys."

Them words skimmed over the prairie sod to where twenty or more of us riders was "throwing the last bait" of the day; and as one and all looked in the direction the talk was coming from, we glimpsed the smiling features of a long cowboy, the straw boss, a-riding in on us and acting like something had sure enough popped. But the grin he was packing had us all sort of guessing; it hinted most to excitement and nothing at all to feel bad about, but there again a feller could never tell by looking at Bearpaw what really did happen. He was the sort of feller who'd grin at his own shadow while getting away from a mad cow, and grin all the more if he stubbed his toe while on the way to the nearest corral poles.

The grin spread into a laugh as he got off his horse and walked into the circle, where we'd been peacefully crooking elbows and storing away nourishment, but now, and since that hombre's appearance, all forks was still and all eyes was in the direction of that laughing gazabo and a-waiting for him to tell.

"You don't seem anyways sad about whatever it is that's a-popping," finally says an old hard-faced Tejano.

"No, I don't," answers that cowboy between chuckles. "I take things good-natured, but *you'll* feel sad, old-timer, when some foreigner drops into camp some of these days and *orders* you to roach the manes of your ponies, and brand calves afoot, and tells you that ropes and stock saddles ain't necessary in handling range stock."

The old Texan just gawked at that, and couldn't talk for quite a spell, but finally, after his thoughts got to settling down to business on what Bearpaw had just said, his opinion of such proceedings come to the top and kicked off the lid.

"Any time I get off my horse and begins to pack myself around on foot after a slick-ear," he howled, "I just don't —not for no man. And as far as anybody coming around and ordering the manes of my ponies to be roached, that wouldn't be orders; it'd be plain suicide for the other feller."

There he stopped for a second and squinted at Bearpaw like as if that cowboy was trying to stir him up for a little fun or something.

"But what in Sam Hill are you driving at, anyway?" he asks.

"I'll be glad to tell you," says Bearpaw, "if you'll give me the chance." Then he went on to spread the news why him and the cow foreman had been called on to the home ranch the last couple of days.

"You boys won't believe me when I tell you," he begins, "but anyway, here's the straight of it: The Y-Bench Y̲ layout is sold out and has done changed hands."

Here he held on a spell, to sort of let things soak in, and looked around at us to see how that part of the news was taking effect. It was taking effect, all right, but we hadn't got anywheres near to realizing what that really meant to us, nor how it all come about, when old Bearpaw follows on with an uppercut that lays us all out.

"Some lord or duke from somewheres in Europe has bought it, and he's brought his stable valets along to show us how to ride. And what's more," he went on, "this here lord, or something, is dead set against these saddles we use, so he's brought along a carload of nice little flat saddles for us, and so light that even a mosquito could stand up under 'em."

Bearpaw would of most likely went on with a lot more descriptions of this lord and other strange things, but he was interrupted by a loud snort from the old Texan, who had managed to come to, right in the middle of the blow.

"All right," he hollered, "I've heard all I want to hear, far as I'm concerned." He got up, throwed his tin cup and plate in the roundup pan with a clatter, and walking away he was heard to say: "I've rode for the Y-Bench for many a year, but I feel it that starting tomorrow I'll be hitting for other countries."

No songs was heard during "cocktail" that evening; no mouth organ was dug up out of the war bag; instead we was all busy a-trying to figger out how the Y-Bench changed hands so quick, and without warning, the way it had. Just a few days before, the cow foreman had remarked that the outfit was figgering on leasing more range and running more stock, and now all of a sudden, and when all seemed to be going well, here comes the news that we had a new owner.

"I bet the reason of the sudden change is due to the big price that was offered," concludes Bearpaw. "I bet the price was so big no sane man would dare refuse it; but what gets me most is how a man such as this lord, what was raised on chopped feed and used to eating out of silver dishes, would want to come out here and get down to tin plates. From all I hear, he's going to run the outfit hisself too."

"Most likely doing it for the sport that's in it," I chips in.

"He'll get plenty of that before he gets through," remarks Bearpaw, "specially if he sticks to them pancake saddles he's brought along."

We done a lot of joking on the subject and kept at it till along about second guard, but the next morning things looked pretty serious. Most of the boys was for quitting without even a look at the new owner and lord, though work was at its heaviest, and riders quitting at that time would sure put things on the kibosh for fair.

The old Texan was the first at the rope corral, and soon as the nighthawk had brought in the remuda, he dabbed his line on his private horses, led 'em to his saddle and bed, and kept a-talking to himself as he fastened the rigging, his mumbling keeping up till a shadow on the ground told him somebody was near. A sour look was on his face as he turned to see Bearpaw, who was standing close by and sort of grinning at him a little.

"Now, Straight-up," says Bearpaw ("Straight-up" was the nickname the older feller liked best; he liked to have it remembered that at one time he was the straight-up rider of that country, and on any kind of a horse), "what's the use of you blazing away half-cocked, and quit this outfit cold like this? Why not sort of look forward to a little excitement and fun with this lord on the job? I'm thinking there's going to be lots of that when he comes, and that's what's making me stick around. Besides, you can never tell, and mebbe this lord is a doggone good feller."

The old cowboy was plumb against it at first and wouldn't

even listen, but as Bearpaw talked on of the possibilities, he got so he'd lend an ear, and soon he was just dubious. Then Bearpaw dug up his hole card and says:

"It sure won't hurt you to stick around just for a few days anyway; and if you do stay, I know I can get the other boys to stay too; besides, I'm thinking you'd miss a lot if you go now."

The Texan thought things over for quite a spell longer and finally he says:

"All right—if you fellers can stick it out, I guess I can too; I'll weather it out with the rest of you."

It was a couple of days later and near sundown when Bearpaw pointed at the sky line to the east and hollered:

"All you cow valets look up there on that ridge and see what's a-coming."

We all looked, and right away forgot what Bearpaw had called us as we took in the sight, for showing up plain against the sky line we could see a loaded wagon coming, and 'longside it a few men on horseback.

"That's him and his outfit," says the old Texan. "It's our lord."

"Gosh-a'mighty," says Bearpaw, "it looks like he even brought a manicure with him, by the size of that escort!"

The outfit came on, and pretty soon two riders started on ahead toward our camp. One of 'em was easy to make out; he was our foreman; the other we figgered to be none less than the new owner.

Redheaded and freckle-faced was His Lordship, and as he come close to be introduced to each of us boys, we noticed that his nose was already beginning to peel. His lower lip had started to crack too, but with all his red hair, freckles, peeled nose and cracked lip, there was something about him that was still unruffled and shiny, even if it was a little dusty, and that was his high-class riding breeches and his flat-heeled riding boots. The little nickel spurs was still a-hanging onto them boots, too, and set 'em off real stylish.

"Well, boys," we hear our foreman say, "I guess Bearpaw told you how the outfit had changed hands; this gentleman here is the new owner of the Y-Bench. I hope that you'll all be as good men with him as you have been with me, and"—here he winked at us—"if a little storm comes up, don't quit too quick, but weather it out like we've always done and don't leave go of the critter till the critter hollers 'Enough.'"

The introduction was no more than over when up comes the wagon all loaded down, and by the side of it two men as peeled as His Lordship, wearing the same kind of pants and boots, and setting on the exact same kind of flat saddles. Them we figgered was the two that was to give us some pointers about riding.

"Seems like," Bearpaw says to me, "that all their saddles and boots and pants and all are made alike; I guess they all have the same taste."

A lot of opinions was scattered to the breeze, on guard that night. Every time a rider would pass another while circling the bedded herd, there'd be a short stop, a remark passed, and the next time the riders met again on the opposite side of the herd that remark would be replaced by another.

The next morning came, and not any too early to suit us, because we wanted awful bad to have them stable valets show us how to mount a horse or something. There was quite a few horses we wanted them to use while they was eddicating us that way, and we was real anxious for all the learning they could hand us.

But the dignified silk tents with their air mattresses and folding cots was showing no sign of any life. It was near sunup too, and Bearpaw, being the straw boss, was near at the point of going to the tent and waking up His Lordship, when the cook stopped him and headed him back.

"You doggone fool, don't you know it ain't proper to bust in when nobility's asleep that way, unless you're ordered to?"

Bearpaw was half peeved when he waved a hand at us boys to saddle up. "Well," he says, "I guess we can get along without him."

Them white silk tents was an awful temptation to all of us as we topped off our ponies and sort of let 'em perambulate around with heads free. A-shining to the sun the way they was, sort of invited initiation, and I think that was the way Bramah Long felt when he sort of hazed his bucking bronc right about dead center for His Lordship's air mattress. All would of went well maybe, only the cook interfered again, and waving a long yellow slicker over his head, came to the nobility's rescue.

As it was, not a snore was disturbed as we rode on past for the day's first ride; even the old Texan's loop was spoiled by Bearpaw as it started to sail for a holt on one of them peaceful tents.

"Mighty doggone nice of you and the cook appointing yourselves as guardians," remarks the old cowboy to Bearpaw. "I thought you told me that we might have a little fun, and here you come along and spoil the best loop I ever spread."

The morning circle was made as usual and the same as if no new foreman had took holt. So far, nothing had come from him to disturb us in any way, and it looked like Bearpaw had, just natural-like, fell into being a cow foreman.

Some folks are just lucky that way, and climb up in the world without half trying.

We made our drive, caught fresh horses, and was working the herd we'd brought in, before we seen anything of His Lordship and the valets. We was all busy cutting out when we notices them a-coming like they was riding on the tail end of a funeral. They was riding the same horses they rode in from the home ranch, and to that the old Texan remarked:

"I guess they never change horses, where they come from."

"I don't think it's that, as much as the fact that they're a little leary of what they might draw out of that corral," says a cowboy near him. "Mebbe them thoroughbreds they're riding looks best to 'em, or safest."

His Lordship and his two men came up to within a hundred yards or so of the herd and from there watched the whole goings on. They sat their horses stiff as statues and gave the feeling that if them horses started right sudden, they'd be left suspended in mid-air and still stiff. Hardly a word or a move of the hand was noticed, and as once in a while one of us would ride by 'em in heading off a bunch-quitting critter, not an eye would seem to notice or recognize any of us.

But them not seeming to see nor recognize us that way wasn't on account of their being stuck-up or such-like; it was that they was so interested in the whole goings on in general that they were satisfied to just set on their horses and watch. Anyway, that's how we took it, for after the work was through and we all sashayed to the chuck wagon, His Lordship and valets all seemed mighty sociable, and asked a lot of questions, most of which was sure hard to answer.

It was as we was cutting the meal short as usual and starting to go toward the corral that His Lordship stopped us and asked where we was going.

"On circle," answered Bearpaw.

"What do you mean by circle?"

"Ride."

"Why, you made one ride already," comes back His Lordship. "Besides, if you're going, I would like jolly well to go with you, but I am only half through with my meal."

"Oh, that's all right," says Bearpaw. "You can catch up with us."

We caught our horses and rode on out for the second circle, and it wasn't till we got sight of camp later that afternoon that we seen His Lordship again. Him and his two men showed up as we was working the herd, and the three of 'em watched us cut out, rope and brand, with the same interest that'd been with 'em that forenoon.

"I tried to catch up with you as you told me," says His Lordship, who'd edged up to Bearpaw, "but it seemed like you men disappeared all at once and I couldn't find you anywhere. I'm afraid," he went on after a spell, "that I make a very poor foreman."

"You'll get on to that after a while," says Bearpaw. "It all takes time."

The work that had to be done kind of kept His Lordship from carrying on the conversation as he'd like to, and it wasn't till the evening meal was over, and the night horses caught, that he had a chance to get down to bedrock with us.

He started with a lot of questions which after they was answered seemed to set His Lordship to doing a lot of figgering. He figgered on for quite a spell, and when he finally spoke again, we already had a hunch of what the subject would be.

"When I bought this ranch," he starts in, "it was with intentions of changing and modernizing the handling of it, to my ideas. Of course, it will take time to do all that, and I might need some advice, but if you men will stay with me while I experiment, I promise that none of you will be sorry."

"Sure," interrupts Bearpaw, speaking for us all. "We'll stick—we'll enjoy it."

I don't think His Lordship got the meaning of that last; anyway he didn't seem nowheres disturbed as he went on:

"The first thing I'd like to do," he says, "is to make way with them heavy and awkward-looking saddles you men use in this country." He was looking straight at the camp-fire as he said that, and it's a good thing he was.

"I think your saddles are altogether unnecessary"—the old Texan snorted, at that—"too cumbersome, and I don't see why they need to be that. We play strenuous games of polo in *our* saddles, jump high fences and do cross-country runs in steeplechases, and I think that, as a whole, we have a freedom to do things from our saddles that you men can't have in yours.

"I have brought some fine pigskin saddles with me for the purpose of you men using them, and tomorrow each one of you will be given one to use in the place of what you are now using."

"That's all very plain," says Bearpaw, a-trying hard to keep cool, "and being you're so frank in telling us about our saddles, I can be frank too and tell you, before you start in modernizing things, that them little stickers you brought along would be worse than riding bareback when there's real work and real riding to be done. I see you don't realize what our saddles mean to us; but anyway, I'll tell you what we'll agree to do. You got two men with you what savvies all about setting on them pancake saddles of yours, ain't you?" asks Bearpaw.

"Yes," answers His Lordship.

"Well," goes on the cowboy, "tomorrow we'll all go to work the same as usual. We'll ride our own cumbersome saddles, and you and your two topnotchers can ride your flyweights. I take it you all have got riding down to a science and it'll be a fair deal. You and your men do what we do, and if, after the day's work is over, you're still with us, we'll agree to use them little saddles of yours and love 'em to death. Is that O. K.?"

"Oh, yes," answers His Lordship, "that will be top-hole."

"And say," hollers the old Texan, "do we get riding habits with them saddles of yours? It sure wouldn't look right to be riding on one of them things and have to wear chaps."

The break of the new day, and all the excitement that it promised, seemed awful slow coming. A faint streak had no more than showed in the east when us all was up and around. A while later we heard the remuda being brought in and corralled by the nighthawk, and we made our way to where the cook had the coffee boiling.

"Say, cook," says Bramah, "better wake up the nobility; it's high time for cowboys to be at work."

But the cook never let on he heard, and there was only one thing for us to do and that was to stick around and wait. There was many a bright remark brought on as the waiting kept up, and all of us was looking forward to the treat we knowed was coming.

The sun was just a-peeping over the ridge, and we should of been ten miles from camp by that time, but it wasn't till then that we begin to hear murmurs coming from the silk tents, and after what seemed an awful long while His Lordship and top hands finally showed themselves.

We'd long ago had our breakfast, so, to rush things a bit, we started out for the corral and begin catching our horses.

"Now, boys," says Bearpaw, "don't all go to catching your worst horses for this event; just catch them that's in turn to be rode; we don't want to make it too hard on His Lordship."

"And it happens that today is the day for Skyrocket," says Bramah, grinning.

Even though we took our time and done a lot of kidding while catching our horses, we still had to wait quite a spell for the nobility to join us. We wanted to give 'em a fair start, 'cause we felt they'd sure need it. But at last, here they come, packing their little pancake saddles.

"Now," says Bearpaw, as His Lordship come near, "according to our agreement of last evening, this contest is to be played on the square. I'm giving you all the best of the deal by letting you pick out your own horses—most of 'em are gentle; and if you pick out a bad one I'll give you the privilege of another pick. Go ahead now and do your picking; I'll rope 'em out for you."

Quite a bit of picking was done before three horses was decided on. The horse His Lordship was to ride was a good-sized bay and one of the best cowhorses in that remuda. He only had one little trick, and that was when first getting on him of mornings, he was apt to do anything but stand still; but outside of that, which is never noticed, that horse was plumb gentle.

The two valets drawed pretty fair horses as to size, but neither one of 'em knowed very much. They was just good "circle" horses. One of 'em would buck, but that was very seldom, and he couldn't buck hard—

The horses all caught, we started saddling, and had to wait some more there. It struck us queer how it took so long to put on one of them little bits of saddles.

Bramah got tired of waiting and got aboard his Skyrocket horse juts "to top him off," as he put it. There was some more delay about then because His Lordship had got all interested in watching that pony buck and Bramah ride.

Finally, the saddling went on again, and the nobility was making ready to mount. His Lordship grabbed his handful of double reins and stepped back to reach for the stirrup, when his horse whirled and went the other way.

The reins being over his head made a jerk on the bit as he whirled that caused him to rear up, and the next second His Lordship let go his holt on the reins.

Bearpaw caught the horse and led him back to His Lordship.

"You don't hold your reins right," he says. "Besides, you've got enough reins and bits on that bridle for a six-horse team."

His Lordship sort of got red in the face at that, but he had no comeback just then; instead, he put his interest in watching Bearpaw, who was showing him how to gather up them reins so he'd have control of his horse while getting on. The style wasn't according to riding schools mebbe, but it was sure convincing, to both man and horse.

It took quite a little trying before His Lordship could get onto the best way of straddling a horse, and he didn't get onto it very well, but with the coaching of Bearpaw, and after catching the horse a couple of times more, His Lordship finally did get in the saddle, and there he was, setting like a knot on a log and a-hanging onto all the reins with a death grip.

All the while that was goin' on, the two valets, who knowed all about riding, had stood in their tracks and watched Bearpaw eddicate their master; then came their turn to climb on. A beller came from the old Texan as he watched 'em reach for their stirrups.

"Where did you-all learn to ride—in a merry-go-round?" he asks. "Don't you know you're apt to get your Adam's apple kicked off a-trying to get on a horse that-a-way?"

Here the old feller got off his own horse and showed 'em what he meant. "Never get back of your stirrup to get on," he says, "not with these horses. If you want to stay all together, stick close to their shoulder and get your foot in the stirrup from there."

The old Texan's talk didn't stand for no argument; every word he said was well took in, and acted on according, because it was realized that what he said was for their own good. One man forked his horse without any trouble much, and that left only one more to contend with.

That last one, though, managed to let his horse go out from under him twice. "It's no wonder," says Bramah, who like the rest of us was watching, "with them iron stirrups a-flapping. I guess they're hard to find."

Near an hour was spent in getting the nobility mounted and ready to go; then Bearpaw took the lead out for the day's first circle.

"We're considerable late getting started this morning," says the cowboy to the cook as we all rode by the chuck wagon, "and don't fix anything to eat till you see us a-coming."

From there we started on a long lope as usual, and as we was going over a pretty level country, all went well. The nobility kept up in fine shape and seemed to enjoy it to the limit. Only once did they slack up some, and that was when a prairie-dog town was crossed. The big holes them dogs made looked like a natural place for a horse to put his foot into and turn a flip-flop. Bearpaw caught 'em up on that slowing down, soon as they got to speaking distance again.

"You'll never turn nor head off a range critter if you keep a-looking at the ground," he says.

The country kept a-getting rougher and rougher as we rode, and pretty soon we begin to get in some badland breaks; it would of been a good goat country, only it was a cow country. A ways further, and on reaching a high knoll, we scattered; I drawed one of the valets as a pardner; Bramah drawed the other; and Bearpaw took it onto hisself to initiate His Lordship in chasing the cow.

With this valet for a pardner I was hearing considerable about fox hunting and cross-country runs, as we rode. There was a lot of words that feller said which had me guessing, and as far as that goes, his whole talk had me listening mighty close, so I could get the drift, but pretty soon, as the country kept a-getting rougher, I didn't have to listen any more. Sliding down badland points seemed to have took the talk out of him.

We rode on till the outside of our territory was reached, and then circled, bringing with us whatever cattle we found. We had upward of sixty head with us and headed for camp in good shape when, spotting another bunch, I left the valet to go get them, telling him to keep the main bunch headed straight for a butte I pointed out.

The cattle had a downhill run and was going at a good clip, and I figgered this valet, being used to chasing wild foxes, sure ought to be able to keep up with spooky range cattle, but as I topped the ridge and got the other bunch and headed 'em down a draw to the main bunch, I was surprised, on looking back, to see that that hombre had lost considerable ground. He was just a-trotting along, and in rougher places would even bring his horse down to a slow walk.

It was either lose the valet or the cattle, and being I didn't want to lose the cattle, I fogged in on them and kept 'em headed straight for the cutting grounds. I figgered the valet would catch up with me soon as we hit level country again, anyway. There was no way of his getting lost, 'cause the cattle and me was sure leaving a good trail and plenty of dust for him to follow.

When I hit level country and looked back, I was surprised how that feller was still so far behind; he was only a little speck in the distance. The cattle had slowed down by then, but even at that, I'd reached the cutting grounds and camp, turned my horse loose, caught me a fresh one and was back to the herd with the other riders before that feller showed up.

"What," I thought, "would of happened if we'd been running mustangs instead of cows?"

"Well, I see you lost yours too," says Bramah, a-riding up and bringing his horse to a stop alongside of mine. "This valet I had done pretty well, though," went on Bramah, "and I didn't lose him till his horse started fighting his head on account of all them bits. I guess he was leary that horse might dump him off any minute."

We was a-talking along, when here comes Bearpaw. That cowboy had no cattle with him but instead, and a ways behind, came His Lordship and that other valet which Bramah'd lost.

The noon meal came in the late afternoon that day, and it was over with quick. Fresh horses was caught all around, and leaving a couple of men to hold the morning's drive, the second circle of the day was started off in another direction.

His Lordship and the two valets wasn't in on the second ride; the thirty-mile circle of that morning'd seemed enough. They was kinda sore and stiff, and the way they'd rub their shinbones went to show that the little narrow stirrup strap on their pancake saddles had developed teeth and dug in from the instep on up. We figgered they'd drawed out of the contest and that they was finding how it was one thing to ride around for sport and when a feller *jolly well* feels like it, and altogether another when that same riding turns out to be *work*.

On account of being delayed that morning, it put us late getting in with our second drive that afternoon, but being we had no nobility to keep track of, we made pretty good time. His Lordship and two men showed up on the cutting grounds soon as we got there, and, mounted on the same horses they'd rode that morning, watched us cut out and brand. Once in a while one of 'em would try to turn back some critter that'd break out, but most always some cowboy would have to ride up and do that little thing for them. They was having a hard time sticking to their saddles as the cowhorse would try to outdodge some kinky critter, and they didn't dare let that horse do his work, from which we figgered that the polo game His Lordship described to us as being so strenuous must be kinda tame after all, compared with the side-winding of a cowhorse working on a herd.

A big red steer broke out once and right in the path of His

Lordship. Being he was there, His Lordship tried to turn him, but Mr. Steer was on the warpath and wouldn't turn worth a nickel. The light that was in that critter's eyes hadn't been at all noticed by that person, but the good old cowhorse he was riding noticed it, and that's how come that when that pony dodged out of the way, His Lordship didn't dodge with him. Instead, he found hisself near straddling that red steer, as he headed for hard ground.

"Doggone queer," says one of the boys, who alongside of me was watching His Lordship shake the dust off hisself, "how a man that's had so much teaching in horsemanship, as they call it, can fall off a horse the way he's done, without that horse even bucking."

"Maybe it's them saddles," I says.

"That has a little to do with it, but he'd a-fell off one of our saddles just the same."

Two grinning riders closest to the bunch-quitting steer started out a-swinging their ropes, with intentions of turning that steer over a few times and to behaving, but Bearpaw, who'd been cutting out, came out of the herd about then and told 'em to put their ropes up and let the steer go.

The boys didn't know what to make of that till Bearpaw explained so everybody could hear.

"We don't want to forget," he says, "that we can't rope and throw a big steer off of them pancake saddles which His Lordship wants us to use, and being we might have to ride on them things later on, we better begin to realize it now, and gradual, so as the shock won't be so sudden."

So the steer was let go, and every other critter which couldn't be turned without the help of the convincing rope. Then that night, while every rider, His Lordship and all, was gathered around the fire, Bearpaw got up in the middle

of the conversation and gave us boys another blow.

"I've cut out two cows and a steer," says that feller, "and they're in the main herd. The cows have their noses full of porcupine quills, and the steer has a horn growing in his eyes. Tomorrow, Bill [pointing at me], you can start out with 'em, take 'em to the home ranch, run 'em through the chute and squeezer, saw the bum horn off that steer and pull the quills out of them cows' noses. You ought to get over there and back in three days. Of course," he adds on, "we could stretch 'em out and do that little job right here, but we'd have to rope 'em, and that's plumb past the usefulness of a pancake saddle. We'd just as well start getting used to that now."

Things went on that way for a few days, and in all that

time no hint was passed that the contest had come to an end. It was plain to see who all was the losers, but so far there was no giving in from nobility. If anything, His Lordship seemed harder-headed about it than ever, and even though the little flat saddles was getting abused something terrible, and stirrup straps and cinch straps kept a-breaking and being patched up with baling wire, there was no sign that they'd ever be set aside.

Then one day Bearpaw got peeved. The wagon had made camp close to a town which was on the skirts of the Y-Bench range, and Bearpaw had rode in and come out with a brand-new saddle which he'd had made to order, before he ever dreamed that pancake saddles would ever come into his life.

Bearpaw rode into camp and straight on to where His Lordship was rubbing some greasy stuff over his burned face and cracked lip.

"See this new saddle?" he begins, and without waiting for an answer went on: "Well, I aim to use it; if not on this range, it'll be on some other. I've given you the best of the deal and tried to show you how worthless your pancake saddles are out here, and you don't seem convinced. So, to-morrow, if you want to go on with the contest, you'll have to ride the average of the horses *we* do, not the gentlest, and I'll bet that before you get through you'll notice the difference between riding out here and riding out in the parks where you come from."

His Lordship listened to all Bearpaw had to say, but not a word came out of him as the cowboy rode away. We was a-wondering if by sunup the next morning we wouldn't be all paid off and hitting for new ranges.

It was near dark, and some time after Bearpaw had left His Lordship, that we noticed him a-talking to his two men,

and after a while seen 'em all going to where three horses
was picketed. We noticed 'em saddle up and ride away, and
at that we wondered some more.

We didn't see 'em come back that night, but we noticed
the next morning that they'd got back all right, because
in the dim light of daybreak we could make out the shape
of their horses picketed in the same place as the night before.

Bearpaw was still het up on wanting to teach the nobility
a thing or two and he drank his black coffee like he had a
grudge against it, but not a word came out of him as he made
biscuits and fried beef disappear, until Bramah, who was the
last man up that morning, came close to the fire and started
reaching for a cup and coffee.

"Did you fellers see what I just seen?" he asks as he filled
his cup.

Receiving nothing but blank looks from all around,
Bramah laid down his cup and says:

"Come on, waddies—I'll show you."

He took the lead, and we followed him to where His
Lordship's three horses was picketed, and then a grin begin
to spread on each face, even on Bearpaw's, for on each one
of them horses was a honest-to-God stock saddle, and on His
Lordship's horse we all recognized the old saddle Bearpaw
had left at the saddle shop in part payment for his new one.

"And look up there," says Bramah, pointing at His Lordship's tent.

We looked, and the grins spread, for floating in the morning breeze from top of each tent was a white flag.

TENTH STORY

FOR A HORSE

Dusty Knight was a bronc peeler (bronco buster), and when that's said about him there's nothing to be took back, for he was at the top at the rough game. Dusty was most always horse-poor, meaning that he always had more horses than he could use; he kept 'em in fine shape, and on one of his horses he could of rode anywhere with the best of 'em and felt proud. If he come acrost a horse that was an exception and to his taste, he'd dicker for him or work out the money in breaking other horses for him, but some way or another he'd get that horse. It was very seldom that he was left with only two saddle horses, as he was now, but them two was his picked best, and few could touch them for looks, speed, and knowledge with rope and cow work. The other horses he'd let go, as good as they was, wasn't quite perfect to Dusty, and of course whatever little flaws they had wasn't found out till they was worked with a herd, maybe a week after he'd dickered for 'em.

Since his dad had took him on his first ride and before Dusty could walk, he'd rode hundreds of different horses, and always at the back of his head, seems like since he was born, there was the picture of one horse he had there, and with the many horses he rode and the thousands he seen he'd kept alooking and watching for that one perfect horse. He hadn't found him as yet; there'd been a little flaw that went against the mind picture he had in all of the best ones he'd picked on.

He was a couple of days' ride out of town, in the thick of good horse range, where he was always bound to be, and while riding through, going no place in particular, he zig-zagged around quite a bit to always look over this and that bunch of range horses he passed near. Sometime soon he'd strike an outfit that wanted some horses broke; such a job was never hard to get, not for such a hand as Dusty was. He could prove his hand quick, too, by just watching him handle and ride one green bronc, just one; after that the job was his.

A job was his on his third day out. He'd struck a big horse outfit and where a man who could break horses well could always get a job. That outfit had plenty of horses to break, tough good ones, and it sure took a bronc-riding fool to line 'em out, because they was the kind that was born with a snort and raised with a buck.

Dusty done his usual fine work of lining out the first bunch, and then, when he run a second bunch in to start breaking, there was one horse in that bunch that come near taking his breath away. It was the horse he'd always had the picture of at the back of his head—the perfect one. The color of him was blood bay, black mane and tail, the blackest that Dusty had ever seen, and that horse's hide shined to the sun the same as dark blood that'd been polished on redwood. It was sure a pretty color. But that wasn't the only thing that agreed with Dusty's taste about that horse. There was the perfect build of him, from his little intelligent-looking head to his little hard hoofs. There was plenty of good body in between, about eleven hundred pounds of it, and all a proportion to what Dusty thought a horse should be.

"That's him, sure enough," says Dusty as he watched the horse snort and run around the corral, "and you just wait till I get his round back shaped to my saddle and his neck working to the rein, I'll be mounted like no king ever was."

Dusty was about right. But as perfect as the horse seemed to be, there was something about him that wasn't cleared yet. That was the brand on him; that brand showed that he belonged to another outfit than the one he was working for, to a horseman by the name of Bill Huff, and Dusty figured he might have a little trouble fixing things so he could call that horse his own.

He was more than aching to start breaking him and see how he'd turn out, but breaking him would only raise the value in the horse, and so Dusty just broke him to lead, because now he was going to ride over and see the owner of that horse, Bill Huff.

He found out from the riders at the ranch that the horse had strayed. It was a good two days' ride to Huff's ranch, and Dusty, being wise to men's weaknesses for good horses, didn't take the horse with him as he saddled up one of his own and started over to see Huff.

Bill Huff had many horses; about half of 'em he would recognize by description; but when Dusty gave as poor a description as he could of that blood bay, he of a sudden perked his ears and didn't finish rolling his cigarette before he asked:

"Where did you see him?"

"Oh, about a hundred miles east of here. He's running

with a bunch of wild horses and I'm thinking he'll be hard to get. I just happened to be riding this way," Dusty went on, "and being I'm circling back now I could maybe catch the horse if you'll sell him cheap enough. I need a pack horse pretty bad."

"Pack horse!" snorted Huff. "Why, man, you'll never find the makings of a better saddle horse in your life. I'll give you fifty dollars to get him and bring him here to me."

That last gave Dusty something to think about. He seen that Bill Huff sure had no intentions of parting with that animal; he also seen how glad he'd been to learn the horse's whereabouts and the relief that he hadn't been stole. It'd been near a year since he'd strayed away.

"Why, I wouldn't take five hundred dollars for that horse," says Huff, "even if he is wild and unbroke."

But Dusty had nowheres near given up the idea of getting that horse. He wasn't built that way. And it was while he was thinking hard and heard Huff say "unbroke" that he thought of a way.

"Have you any horses here you'd want broke?" he asks.

"Yes," says Huff, "quite a few, and the blood bay is one of 'em. Are you out for a job breaking horses?"

"If I can get enough horses to make the job worth while."

"I can rake up about thirty head easy, and if you're good enough hand I'll pay you extra for breaking the blood bay."

That went well with Dusty. With the scheme he had in mind, even though it would take time to put it through, he seen where sooner or later the bay horse would be his. He loped back to the outfit where he'd been working, drawed what money he had coming, caught his other horse and the blood bay, and in five days' time was back to Bill Huff's outfit.

There he went to work on the first ten head of broncs that was run in, and keeping in mind that he had to prove himself a good hand before he could get the blood bay to break, he brought out all his art at the game. The first few he started got the benefit of that, and in a easy way that made Bill Huff wonder, it seemed to him that them fighting broncs was no more than run in when the rough seemed to be took off of 'em overnight and a little girl could ride 'em. After a few days of watching such goings on, Bill decided that Dusty would sure do in handling his prize blood bay.

And Bill wasn't disappointed. Dusty took that horse, right away gave him the high-sounding name of Capitan before Huff could give him one, and was as careful of his hide as though it was made of diamond-inlaid gold lace. Capitan behaved fine for a green, high-strung bronc and bowed his head to buck only at the first few saddlings. He was quick to learn to turn at the feel of the hackamore rein, and his little chin quivered with nothing, seemed like, only by being anxious to tell ahead of time what was wanted of him and before the mecate knot touched the nerves of his jaws. His little pin ears worked back and forth as alive as his flashing eyes to what all was around him. Dusty still felt him to be the perfect horse, and to Bill Huff he was a dream that'd come to life.

All went fine for a week or so. Dusty rode the other broncs as their turns come, along with Capitan. And then, being Capitan was coming along so good, Dusty told Huff that he was going to turn him loose for a few days, that it would do the horse good and give him time to think things over; besides, he wanted more time to line out the other broncs so he would be done with 'em quicker.

Capitan run loose in a meadow of tall grass for a whole

week, and, as Dusty expected and hoped for, that horse had accumulated a lot of kinks in that time. If that pony thought things over, it was towards how to buck good and nothing else.

It seemed that way to Bill, anyway. He was there when Dusty rode him time and again, and there hadn't been a one saddling when the horse didn't buck, and harder every time.

"Take it out of him, Dusty!" Bill Huff would holler, as Capitan would buck and beller around the corral. "Take it out of him, or, by gad, I'll kill him!"

That last would make Dusty grin to himself. He was now getting the horse to act the way he wanted him and so that Bill Huff wouldn't want him. Dusty would let on that he was also disappointed in the horse and act for all the world as though he was trying his best to take the buck out of him. He'd pull on the reins and slap with the quirt, and the pulls was easy and so was the slaps, and, at the side where Bill wouldn't see, Dusty was only encouraging the horse to buck a little harder.

Capitan didn't need much encouraging; it was in his system to buck anyway, and he always felt like he had something off his chest when he done a good job at it. He'd been just as good in other ways and as a cow horse if that bucking instinct had been left to sleep, as it had before he'd been turned loose for a week; but after that week, and with Dusty giving him his head to do as he pleased while Bill Huff wasn't watching, he'd humped up and bucked a little. Dusty could of easy broke him off of that right then, but it was part of his scheme to have him buck, and when Capitan didn't see no objections coming from his rider he fell into bucking in great style. Now it would take a heap of convincing by a mighty good rider to make him quit.

The horse was acting in great shape for Dusty, and Bill Huff had stopped coming to the corral when he was being rode. Bill had wanted that horse for himself, but he was too old to ride such as he'd turned out to be, and he was fast losing hope of his ever being of any use to him.

"He'll always buck," he says to Dusty one day.

Dusty had walked away and grinned. A few more days now and maybe Bill could be talked into selling the horse to him.

All was going fine, and then one day, before Dusty got to dickering for Capitan, a hammer-headed fifteen-dollar bronc bucked too high, and his feet wasn't under him when he hit the ground, but Dusty was. The horse had turned plumb over while in the air and come down on his back.

Dusty didn't come to his senses soon enough to talk to Bill about Capitan. When he come to he was stretched out in the back of an automobile and headed for town and hospital.

He laid in the hospital for a few months, wabbled around town for one or two more, and when he was able to ride again he hit for Bill Huff's.

Capitan wasn't there no more, and Bill Huff went on to tell how it come about. When Dusty was laid up in the hospital he hired another bronc fighter to take his place and finish up on the batch of broncs that he'd started. That new feller was a pretty fair hand and he handled the broncs all right, all but Capitan. That horse had been loose for a couple of weeks and when he caught him he soon found he couldn't ride him. Capitan had kept agetting worse every time he was rode at. Other riders had tried him with no better luck than the first, and when there came rumors of a rodeo being pulled off in town, one of the boys was for taking that horse to it and let him buck there. He was entered as a tryout bucking horse, and he'd bucked so well that before the contest was over that horse had been promoted to a final horse, amongst the hardest of the buckers. Then Bill Huff had sold him as a bucker for two hundred dollars.

Well, it seemed like Dusty had sure done a good job in giving Capitan the free rein. He'd given him so much free rein that it now looked like he'd never catch up with him. But Dusty had nowheres near given up the chase. Capitan was the one horse in a lifetime to him, the one perfect horse, and of the kind he'd sort of lost hope of ever running across.

If he hadn't had the bad luck of a knot-headed bronc falling on him and laying him flat, Capitan would now be his instead of belonging to somebody else and being shipped from one rodeo to another as a bucking horse. It didn't matter to Dusty if Capitan had turned bucker; he was a young horse and he'd get over that. The main thing that worried him was if the new owner would part with him.

It wasn't many days later when he seen that new owner and found out he wouldn't part with Capitan for no love nor money. It was while a rodeo was going on, and when Dusty seen that horse buck he seen plenty of reasons why he couldn't be bought. Capitan had sure turned wicked.

Dusty was in a worse fix than ever towards getting that horse now. But he didn't lose sight of him. He followed him to two more rodeos, and his heart sort of bled every time he seen him buck out into the arena. That horse, he felt, was too much horse to be no more than just a bucker. It had been his intentions to take that out of him soon as he got him away from Bill Huff and make a top cow horse out of him; he had the brains and Dusty knowed he'd of made a dandy.

Being he hadn't as yet got over his injuries, Dusty didn't

compete in the rodeos. He just stuck around. And one day it came to him to ask Tom Griffin, the owner of the bucking stock, for a job helping in the shipping and taking care of the bucking horses. He had to follow along to two more rodeos before he got that job, and by the time he worked at it for a month or so, Griffin was so pleased with Dusty that after the last rodeo of the season was pulled off he gave him the job of taking care of the bucking horses for the whole winter and till the season opened up again next early summer. Dusty was happy and felt he now had a mane holt towards what he was after.

Dusty was alone at a camp that winter. He had charge of sixty head of bucking horses and fifty head of Mexico longhorns that was used for bucking, roping, and bulldogging. The stock run out on good range, and in case of bad weather there was hay by the corrals for him to feed to 'em. He had plenty of grub and smoking and he was all set.

It was during that winter that Dusty went to doing something that made him feel sort of guilty. He was in good shape to ride again by then, and it would of struck anybody queer that knowed the bucking horses, more so Griffin, if they'd seen him pick on the worst one in the string, Capitan, and go to riding that horse.

But Dusty wasn't out for the fun of riding a bucker when he straddled Capitan; he was out to make that horse quit being a bucker and make him worthless as such, and that's what made him feel guilty. He was spoiling his boss' best bucking horse by taking the buck out of him.

The only consolation Dusty had was by repeating to himself that there was lots of good bucking horses and that Capitan was too good to be one, and when the thought came to him that that horse would most likely be his after the first rodeo was pulled off, that sort of washed away all the guilty feelings he might of had.

Dusty about earned that horse before the hard bucking jumps at every saddling dwindled down to crow hops. Spring was breaking and Capitan still had plenty of buck in him, and any rider that could of went so far with such a horse was sure worth a heap of consideration, because few of 'em ever stayed over a few jumps while that horse bucked in the arenas. Of course there the riders had to ride by rules, and it's harder to sit a bucking horse that way than it is when there's no rules and all you have to do is stay on top.

By the time the snow all went away and the grass got tall and green, Dusty was using Capitan for a saddle horse, and what a saddle horse he turned out to be! As good as he'd been a bucking horse, and that's saying something. And now the only thing that worried Dusty was how Griffin was going to take it when he seen that horse come out of the chute and not buck, or would he go to bucking again? If he did there'd be no hope of Dusty ever owning him.

The day came when all the stock was gathered and preparations was made for the first rodeo of the year. Capitan didn't look like he'd ever had a saddle on that winter, and with the care that Dusty gave him—extra feeds of grain and all—he was as round and fat as a seal. Griffin looked at him and smiled.

But that smile faded when that horse came out of the chute on that first rodeo, for Capitan just crow-hopped a couple of jumps and trotted around like the broke saddle horse he was. The cowboy hooked him a couple of times and all he could get out of him was a couple more gentle crow hops. That cowboy had to get a reride on another bucking horse so he could qualify. Dusty was just as happy as Griffin was surprised and disappointed. Griffin couldn't figure out how that horse quit bucking, for he'd expected him to be a top at that for quite a few years. He couldn't suspicion Dusty of having anything to do with it; he'd never seen Dusty ride and it would never come to his mind that any cowboy could take the buck out of such a horse, not when that horse had it in him so natural.

But Griffin wasn't going to lose hope of that horse ever bucking again. He put him in the tryouts twice a day. Capitan didn't at all do at first, but before the last day of the contest came it looked like he was beginning to turn loose and go to bucking again. Griffin begin to smile and Dusty begin to worry.

It was two weeks before time for another rodeo. In that time Dusty took charge of the horses again and held 'em in a pasture not far out of town. It was there that Dusty took the buck out of Capitan once more. It was easier this time because he hadn't accumulated much.

The same thing happened at the second rodeo as with the first. Capitan wouldn't buck, and every cowboy that came out on him wanted a reride, "on a bucking horse," they said, "not a saddle horse."

Capitan began to loosen up some more before the end of that second rodeo; but by the time Dusty got through with him in the three weeks before the next rodeo that horse was scared to buck, and when that third contest did open up and Capitan couldn't be made to buck was when Griffin sort of lost his temper. The cowboys had been digging into him about bringing in gentle horses and trying to make bucking horses out of 'em, remarking that they was tired of asking for rerides and so on, till finally, when Capitan came out of the chute once more and only humped up as a cowboy hooked him, he lost his temper for good and passed the remark that he'd take two bits for that horse.

Dusty was standing close by, expecting him to say such a thing.

"I'll do better than that, Tom," he says. "I've got fifty dollars in wages coming that I'll give you for him."

Tom hardly looked at him. He scribbled out a bill of sale and passed it to Dusty. Dusty folded the bill of sale, stuck it in a good safe pocket of his vest, and started to walk away. Tom sort of star-gazed at him as he did, still dazed by the way Capitan quit bucking after every rodeo. Then, as he watched Dusty walk away so spry, the whole conglomeration came to him as clear as day. He was the one that wanted the horse.

"Hey, Dusty!" he hollered. Dusty stopped and looked back. "You're fired," he says.

"I know it," says Dusty, grinning, and walked on.

Capitan was led out of the bucking string of horses, saddled, and peacefully rode out of town. When the lanes was left behind and open country was all around, Dusty ran his fingers through the silky mane of the bay and says:

"All is fair in love as in war."

ELEVENTH STORY

SILVER MOUNTED

"Howdy!" We turned at the voice of a stranger who, outside and setting on a good-looking bay horse, was looking at us through the camp's only window, and smiling.

Strangers was mighty scarce in that country, and mighty welcome; and when Long Tom, our foreman, returned that stranger's "howdy," it was natural-like followed with "Turn your horse loose and come on in."

It was a while later when a shadow was throwed acrost the door and the stranger walked in, and still a-smiling begin unsnapping his batwing chaps.

"We just got in a few minutes ago," says Long Tom, "and the cooky's got 'er all ready. Go ahead and wash up; we'll wait for you."

The stranger had gone to the washbench outside, when Little Joe leaned my way and in a low voice asks: "Say, Bill, did you see the boots that hombre's wearing? And look at them chaps," he goes on while fingering of 'em. "Soft as silk, and with silver mountings."

I sure had noticed them boots; they was the kind any cowboy would glance at more than once. The flower design that was on 'em, in inlaid colored leather and bordered with many rows of fancy stitching, would attract a blind man. The soft kangaroo vamp, with the well-shaped, not too high heel, sure had my eye too. The chaps was of gray soft leather, the wing covered with leather designs, and pure silver ornaments on the belt and more along the wing.

"It'd be a shame to use an outfit that in this sunburnt lava and sagebrush country," says Joe. "It'd sure skin the pretty spots off it in no time."

The stranger, all washed and hair combed, walked in again, and all of us trailed over to the long table to partake of the last meal of the day. The talk was as usual, and not ruffled any by the presence of the stranger. Once in a while he'd inquire some about the country, and his talk fitted in well. Before the meal was over, and without asking any questions, we had him figgered out as a rider from the prairie countries, but we wasn't sure. A few days would tell, and we hoped he'd stick around, for we'd sort of took a liking to his ways, fancy outfit and all.

It was early the next morning when a few of us boys was at the corrals and rolling that day's first cigarettes. The remuda hadn't got in yet, and while waiting, we run acrost the stranger's rig. A real fancy saddle it was, all hand-carved and weighed down with silver, and on the rosaderos was letters saying: *For First Prize in Bucking Contest.*

Them carved letters sort of identified the stranger to us, but there was other things about the outfit that was a puzzle and which didn't match none at all. Like for instance, there was a real well made saddle with a neat little silver horn, bare and for tying, and instead of having the hard-twist grass rope coiled up on the side of that saddle, and which was the only kind that belonged there, there was a sixty-foot rawhide reata, plumb useless, and not at all fitting with it nor the slick horn that was on it.

His bridle didn't agree no better; the headstall belonged to Wyoming, the bit to Mexico, and the rawhide reins to the California Spanish. None ever go together, and it was sure a puzzle to us how that waddy worked or where he was from.

But we was soon to know. The remuda was being drove in the big corrals, and about that time we spots Long Tom coming down with the stranger. Our hopes that he'd stick around went up to the top as we seen the foreman pointing out a string of ponies for him to ride; and seeing it was settled that he was going to be with us for a spell, we all went after our ropes and begin snaring our ponies for that morning's ride.

Our ponies was all caught, saddled, and ready to "top off" when we see the stranger circling a rope over his head and trying to run the horse he wanted, with a "Missouri throw." He was using a braided cotton rope, the kind that's used in spinning, and we figgered the rawhide reata that was on his saddle was only for an ornament.

To begin with, we seen he was no roper, not while he was on the ground, anyway. Long Tom watched the proceedings of the whirling rope for quite a spell; he didn't want to tell the new hand not to whirl his rope in a corral full of horses, on account he figgered the stranger ought to know that without being told, but he didn't like to see the ponies getting all jammed up and skinning their hips on the corral poles, either. He was just about to flip his rope and catch the stranger's horse for him, when he stopped and seen that hombre do a funny thing. The stranger, after missing three or four throws in the "Missouri swipe" fashion, had coiled up his rope and built another loop; and instead of whirling it this time, he begin to spin it. He kept a-spinning it till the horse he wanted circled around the corral and came within roping distance, and about that time the spinning loop shot out, never losing its circle, and caught that pony under the chin, and then the loop settled over his ears.

Long Tom and all of us grinned, looked at one another and shook our heads. The throw the stranger had just made matched well with his fancy boots, chaps and saddle: it was fancy too. But it seemed like there was no end of puzzling things about the stranger, and the next to happen was after we'd topped off our ponies and all of us was ready to line out of the corral gate. I was somewhat surprised, after I made my horse quit sweeping the corral with his foretop, to see that the new hand hadn't saddled his horse yet; he was just a-hanging on to him, wondering what to do, and seemed like looking around for something he could find. Finally, he looked at Long Tom, who was setting on his horse and waiting.

"Is there a chute I can saddle this horse in?" he asks.

The horse he'd caught was a spooky little sorrel and a fighter, and he wouldn't let the stranger come any closer than a safe ten feet from him. He wasn't the worst horse that outfit had, not by a long shot, but he wasn't the gentlest, either. The foreman sized the stranger up for a spell and finally says:

"We saddle our horses in the middle of the corral or any-wheres we get 'em—*out here.*"

I looked at Long Tom as he said them last two words, and had a hunch right then that he knowed what kind of a man he was talking to. That was more than the rest of us could figger out.

Having no time to waste, Long Tom got off his horse, walked over to the stranger and told him to get his saddle. While the stranger was gone, the foreman flipped the loose end of the rope around the spooky sorrel's front feet and hobbled him; then he reached for the saddle that'd been brought up, put it on the slick back and cinched 'er up.

We felt sort of sorry for the stranger as that went on, for we could see that he didn't know what to do with his hands, and he just sort of kept fidgeting around, careful not to look at any of us; but he brightened up some as Long Tom handed him the bridle rein and told him, "It's up to you now."

The stranger seemed glad of it, and the way he climbed that pony showed me he was aching to prove that he was some entitled to that fancy outfit of his.

It was when the little sorrel bogged his head and went after the stranger that we got another surprise, and which made the puzzle all the harder to figger out. The stranger had seemed at home from the time the horse side-winded out of his tracks, and it was then we understood how it was he brightened up when Long Tom handed him the reins and told him to go ahead. That boy could ride.

He reefed that pony and made a fool out of him as well as Little Joe could, and Joe was about the best rider in the outfit. It made a mighty pretty sight too, to which that new hand ride on that fancy outfit. The silver was a-shining to the sun at every curve of the horse's body; the long hand-carved tapaderos, along with the wide wings of the rider's chaps, sort of made the movements of the horse and man mighty easy to watch; and even old bronc-fighting Long Tom had to stand there like the rest of us and admire.

Finally the show was over, and a little too soon to suit us, but we figgered there'd be some more later, as that outfit sure had plenty of mean ponies. We all filed out of the corral, and the stranger amongst us, a-riding along like he was sure a credit to that outfit he was setting on.

We loped out of camp, Long Tom in the lead and never looking back. Three or four miles out, the ponies was brought down to a walk; the gait was kept to that for a mile or so, and into a long lope we went again. A knoll twelve miles or so from camp was reached, and there Long Tom "scattered the riders" different directions—two up a creek, two more over a ridge, and so on, till all the boys was scattered in fan shape to hunt and run in whatever horses was in that country.

The "Double O" was a horse outfit, and run over ten thousand head of the finest horses a man wants to see. It took a big range to run that many horses, and the proof that it was big and also good was by the kind of horses that was raised there. They showed they had all the chance in the world to develop and grow full size, and they was wild, as wild as any horse ever gets, and if it wasn't that they was corralled once or twice a year, they'd soon turn into renegades, for even as it was, it took a mighty good hand who knowed horses, and he had to be well mounted, before he could turn a bunch of them and bring 'em towards the corrals.

As Long Tom scattered the riders, I'm thinking that most every one of us wished to be "paired off" with the stranger: he was such a surprising cuss, and if he could sashay horses like he rode the sorrel, that'd sure be another show well worth watching.

Most of the riders rode away two by twos, till there was

only me and Joe, the stranger and Long Tom left. Then the foreman spoke again.

"Bill," he says, "you, and you [pointing to the stranger] take Lone Mountain, and me and Joe here'll skirt around Rye Patch."

I grinned at Joe and rode away, the stranger for my pardner. We rode along a-talking of nothing in perticular and everything in general. I was wanting awful bad to get an inkling, so as to clear the puzzle he was to me and all of us, but no hinting would make him give any information, and it sure never came to me to come right out and ask him, 'cause you can never tell what a feller's hiding in his upper story or what he's trying to keep as *past*.

To sort of make him feel that I wasn't wanting him to talk on hisself unless he wanted to, I turned the confab towards the present and says:

"You want to watch that sorrel you're riding; he ain't through with you yet, and is apt to bog his head and go after you just when you least expect or want him to. But," I says afterward, "I guess you don't mind that."

I expected him to grin at me in a way that'd show he wasn't caring what the sorrel done or when he done it, and there is where I got another surprise; for the stranger, instead of grinning as any cowboy would at my remark, seemed to turn pale, and then I noticed how he wasn't setting straight up and free, as he had when first leaving the corral. He was setting close now, and with a short tight holt on the reins.

We skirted the foot of Lone Mountain and then wound our way up it; it was a steep and high old mountain and could always be depended on for a couple of bunches of wild, highland-loving ponies. We was halfway up, and I was keeping my eyes peeled to see the wild ones *first*, when on a ridge that run to the mountain, and away up, I spots the buckskin rump of one horse, and I figgers there's a bunch with him.

I stops my horse and points his whereabouts to the stranger and asks: "See that horse up there?"

"Yes," he says, and he was looking away to one side of where the buckskin was; he wasn't seeing him at all.

"Well—anyway," I says, "you keep about the middle of this mountain, and when I start the bunch, I'll head 'em down your way, and you can keep 'em going on down towards the flat."

"All right," he says.

"Doggone queer," I says to myself as I rode away. "He's a top hand in some things, and a pure greenhorn in others. Now, he's never hunted stock much, or he'd sure seen that horse up there; and then again, his acting scared on a horse he *knows* he can ride, sure is past me figgering out."

I maneuvered around till I got on the other side of the bunch I'd spotted, and when I got to the right place, I showed up sudden and fogged in on 'em so quick that them ponies just got scared and flew straight away to where I wanted 'em to go—they didn't have time to stop and parley on how would be the best way to lose me; they just went.

There was about fifteen head in the bunch, and one "marker" amongst 'em identified 'em as Double O horses. I camped on their tail for a ways and till I made sure they was headed past where the stranger should be; he'd keep 'em from doubling back up the mountain, I figgered, and fog 'em on down to the flats as I'd told him to.

Taking another look at the bunch so as to make sure of their going straight down the mountain, I sat on one rein, brought my running bronc to the crowhopping standstill,

and then made him head back, up the mountain. There was another bunch I'd spotted up there. I circled around and on up, losing no time, 'cause I wanted to get that second bunch and throw it with the first so as I could help the stranger in case he needed it; but realizing what a big head start he had on me, I had no hopes much of seeing him and the first bunch till I reached camp.

It took me quite a while to reach the top of that mountain; it was steep and high, and I didn't want to rush my horse too much on account of the run I figgered I'd have to make to get that bunch in. I let him take a good breathing spell when the top was reached, and while I uncinched my saddle and cooled his back a little, I took a look down the flat away below me for a sign of the dust the first bunch I'd started would be making. I had a mighty good view of the country from up there; it all looked like a big map a-stretching with the edges petering out into atmosphere. I could see the fringe of cottonwoods by the camp we'd left that morning, and the creek a-shining in the sun, but in all that landscape I couldn't see no dust. I wondered if the stranger could of got his bunch to camp already and while I was climbing the mountain; it could happen easy enough, 'cause there was nothing slow about them ponies once you got after 'em, and then again that stranger was so surprising, he might be a wizard at running wild ponies.

I got on my bronc and lined him out in a fast walk towards the other bunch. I didn't see no more chance of having the interesting company of the stranger, and I was sorry for that. Anyway, I kettled the other ponies from the right side and fogged 'em on down a long ridge that stretched away out on the flat. It was a fine place to run, and my horse was a-fighting his head to get in amongst the bunch that was raising the dust ahead of him. All was going fine and to order, and I figgered at that speed I'd be in camp in a short spell, when in the canyon to the left I sees a big dust and another bunch of running ponies. They was headed straight up the mountain and the opposite direction I was going, and then I got a glimpse of the buckskin horse, the one I'd first spotted, and then the marker, which told me plain that there was the bunch I'd turned over to the stranger.

"What t'hell, now!" I says as I rode off the edge of the

ridge I was on and into the canyon. I was hoping to turn
'em and throw 'em in with my bunch. The next half a mile
I covered was sure no bridle path, and the speed I made it
in went to show what a doggone fool a feller can be when
getting het up on the subject. I'd turned my horse off into
a straight down run, and the little shelves of shale rock that
was here and there was all that kept us from going down
faster than we did.

But I got in the canyon before the bunch passed me, and
that was the cause of my hurry, for if the bunch had ever
got above me, I'd just as well waved my hat at 'em and let
'em go. I'd never been able to turn 'em.

As it was, they'd had to go through me to get away, and
they'd been handled enough so they didn't try it. They
turned, went down the canyon a ways; then, when the sides
of the ridge wasn't so steep no more, I turned 'em once again
and up on the ridge where the other bunch was still going
strong and the right direction.

Both bunches'd had quite a bit of running; they wasn't so
hard to handle no more, and I had no trouble much getting
'em all together. All was going fine once more; my bronc
had quit fighting his head and a-trying to get in amongst
the horses; he was glad to just lope along behind a ways
and just follow 'em.

I loosened up on the mecate (hair rope) reins and rolled
me a cigarette; then it comes to me: "What's become of the
stranger?"

I looked at the country around as I rode, but no sign of
him was anywheres; then I looked at the bunch which was
keeping ahead of me about a quarter of a mile, and running
my eye over 'em, I thought I seen something a-shining to
the sun and on one pony's back; something else was a-flap-

ping on each side of him. And doing some tall wondering, I rode a little faster so as to have a closer look.

It was hard to make out through the dust, but as I looked on and squinted I finally made out the shape of a saddle; but what bothered me was them things a-shining on top. Then I come near kicking myself for forgetting and being so dumb: them shining things was *silver;* it was the stranger's saddle, and under it was the sorrel he'd rode so well in the corral that morning!

I stopped my horse as the thought came to me that somewheres was the stranger, afoot, and maybe with some bones broke; for when a rider sees a horse packing an empty saddle out on the range, it sure sets him to thinking. A man can petrify out there and never be found only maybe by coyotes or magpies. Fifteen or twenty miles is a long ways with a smashed-up leg.

Of course the stranger might be all right, I thought, but there's no telling where he may be laying and crippled from a fall. There was only one thing for me to do; I fogged in on my bunch and took 'em as fast as I could. Halfways in, I could see the dust of other bunches being brought in by other riders, and I turned my bunch to meet one of the closest.

Throwing my bunch in with 'em, I stopped just long enough to tell the two boys that was hazing 'em in that the stranger's horse was in the bunch I'd brought in and he was afoot somewheres. Then I headed on the back trail to look for him.

I picked up his trail where I'd left him and followed it along a ways. I seen where he stopped his horse and waited for me to head the first bunch down his way. From there on, the tracks of his horse was far apart: he'd been running him and, as I figgered, taking after the bunch as they come.

I followed that trail for quite a while; it was doing a lot of zigzags, and I could see that the bunch was somehow getting away from him and back up the mountain; then of a sudden I seen a patch of tore-up ground. It'd been tore up by the hoofs of the little sorrel, and in the middle of that patch was something that made me get off my horse for a closer look. There, as pretty as you please, was the print of the stranger's body where he'd connected with Mother Earth and measured his length. The stranger had been throwed off.

That was hard for me to believe, but there, and right in front of me, was plain proof. I took another long look at the tore-up patch, then got on my horse and went to cutting for tracks which would tell me where the stranger went. One thing I was mighty glad for, and that was he wasn't hurt, and when I run onto the trail he'd left with them neat heels on them pretty boots of his, I could see he was walking straight up and not staggering any, far as I could make out.

His trail crossed a creek, and there I felt better some more, for he'd had water anyway, in case he needed it. Acrost the creek, a few miles wide, many miles long and running toward camp, was a strip of lava rock. No earth was there to follow a trail, and I lost track of him, but I figgered he'd be following the lava strip back to camp, on account it might be a little easier walking there.

I rode on back towards camp following it, and feeling sure I'd run acrost him before he got in, but I rode many miles, and no stranger was seen. A little ways further, I spots the boys riding up; they'd started out looking for him too.

After I told 'em where I left his trail, they rode on to look for him; my horse was tired, and I went on into camp.

The boys didn't get back till way after dark, and no sign of the stranger had been found. We built a big log fire by the camp that night and where it could be seen for miles around. It would burn a long time, and if the stranger was within ten miles, he couldn't fail but see it. We couldn't do no more.

The fire burned down; morning came, and still no sign of the stranger. Two riders was sent out to look for him that day, and when night come and they rode back, the disappearance of that hombre was still as much of a puzzle as ever. It seemed like the earth had just swallowed him. Another day went by, and it was as the mountains was throwing long shadows that Joe points out to a dust acrost the flats. A rider was making it.

The last horse had been unsaddled as the rider came up to the corral gate and got off his horse. It was the stranger, but a very different-looking stranger than he'd been a few days past and when he'd made his first appearance at the horse camp. There was a stub growth of whiskers and hollow cheeks on a face that'd been round and smooth, and the alkali dust that covered him from head to foot sure done the work of disfiggering all he'd been to look at.

We all greeted him as though nothing had happened, and not a question was asked; we didn't have to ask, on account that there was everything about him that told us all we cared to know and plainer than words. It was all easy reading, the same as the print he'd left in the foothills and where the sorrel throwed him off.

The horse he'd rode in wore the brand of a neighbor outfit which was some thirty miles away, and knowing he couldn't of caught him on the range with a saddle on him and all that way, it was easy to see he'd rambled on afoot for some time till he come to one of that neighbor outfit's camps, borrowed the horse, and got his directions to come back on from there. Yes, sir, the stranger had went and got lost.

It was sure a mystery to us how a man that could ride like he'd rode the sorrel, and do such fancy roping as he'd done, could turn out to be such a freak. "How and where," we'd ask one another, "can a man learn to ride like he could, if it ain't on the range?" Nobody could answer that, and the mystery instead of getting any clearer with reasoning, kept a-getting deeper.

The next day came, and a long ride was ahead for that morning. The stranger showed up at the corral and we seen him make his spinning loop with a lot of interest. That interest went up many notches as we seen that same loop settle around the head of a tall, rawboned brown horse. That horse was one of the meanest buckers in the outfit and didn't belong to his string none at all; but he'd mistook him, amongst the two hundred ponies, for one that'd been pointed out to him that first morning.

"I guess you don't want him," says Long Tom, riding up. "He ain't in your string, and besides, he's sure hell on wheels when it comes to bucking."

"Whose string is he in?" asks the stranger.

"Nobody's; we take turns at him once in a while, and he's for anybody that wants him."

"Well, I guess I'll try him, then, if I can get somebody to help me saddle him."

He got all the help he wanted, and in less time than it takes to tell it, the saddle and bridle was on the big horse, and the blindfold ready to take off soon as the stranger was well set. The hombre climbed on not a bit ruffled, and when ready, he told us so in a way that would make us put our money on him.

The blindfold was yanked off, and it was no more than done when the tall gelding called on his wiry frame to do its duty. Two spurred heels went up in the air about the time the horse did, and when that pony buried his head in the dirt in a hard-hitting jump, them spurred heels came down on his neck and played a ringing tattoo there.

Between the bellering of that horse, the ringing of the spur rowels, the sound of that pony's hoofs hitting the earth —all a-popping, and keeping time—it sure made a sound worth sticking around for by itself; and even if a man couldn't of seen the goings on, he could of told by them sounds that here was a hard horse to ride, and on top of him was a hard man to throw.

The stranger seemed in the height of his glory; he was setting up there, and fast and crooked as the jumps came, he wasn't caught napping at any of 'em. He met that pony halfways in all he done, and when finally the big gelding seemed to have enough and held his head up, we'd forgot that the man on top of him had let a little sorrel horse buck him off, we'd forgot that he'd let a bunch of horses get away from him on the range, and even his getting lost and roaming straight away from the home camp seemed away in the past. The stranger was one of us again.

We filed out of the corral and strung out on the morning's circle. Me and the stranger was riding side by side and by ourselves a ways; I expected that brown horse to go to bucking again most any time, and sure enough, Long Tom had no more than started us out in a lope, when I glimpses a brown hunk of horseflesh transformed into a cloud-reaching and then earth-pounding whirlwind. I heard the beller

of the pony, but I didn't hear no spurs ringing, and when I looked for the reason, I was surprised to see that them spurs wasn't at all where I thought they'd be—on the horse's neck. Instead of that they was buried in the cinch with a staying holt, and I thought for a second that I seen the stranger grabbing for the horn.

Little Joe, who'd been to one side a ways, rode close about that time, and I noticed the blank look on his face, like he didn't believe his eyes; and my face must of showed about the same look as I stared back at him, 'cause I know I was sure as surprised as he was.

Somehow I was glad when the brown horse quit bucking and lined out on a lope with the stranger *still* on him; I sort of hated to get disappointed in that feller, and I could see that Joe felt the same about it; but we both could see that it was pure luck the stranger hadn't been bucked off—he'd rode his horse like a rag and hung on with a death grip.

"That feller seems like a different man outside a corral," Joe remarked as we rode on, a-trying to figger out the puzzle.

Long Tom done a mighty fine job of scattering the riders that day; most every man wound up by hisself, and none of us got to see one another again till the circle was made and we was within a few miles of the corral wings. Every man had a bunch, and some two, and when the gate closed on the last bunch that was run in, we all natural-like begin to take a tally on one another, to see if any was missing.

It was then that Long Tom points at me and Joe and says: "You two better change horses; take an extra one along and go look for the stranger. I'm thinking he's afoot again." Yep, the stranger was amongst the missing once more!

It was pure luck when we found him, near sundown. Joe

had spotted an object up on the ridge that first looked like
a prospector's monument, and when we rode up on it, it
turned out to be the stranger a-setting on his saddle. His
clothes was near all tore off of him, and the fancy saddle
looked like it'd run up against a buzz saw; it was all twisted
out of shape and caked with dirt.

The stranger's spirit was sort of low too, but he managed
to smile as he seen us, and halfhearted-like told us how the
brown horse had bucked him off.

"But what happened to your saddle?" asks Joe.

"Well, I guess that's my fault," goes on the stranger. "I
never figgered that a cinch gets loose as a horse runs and
gants up. I'd been running him up a slope and the saddle
slipped back. After he bucked me off, it turned under his
belly, and, as you see, that pony sure done a good job kicking it apart."

We all rode on back to camp, not saying much. I'd glance
at the stranger once in a while, and I could see that feller
was thinking about something mighty strong. I wished he'd
let us in on his thoughts, but it wasn't till we'd near reached
camp that he seemed to want to loosen up.

"I can't figger it out," he says.

"What's that?" asks Joe.

"Well," he goes on, "it's the difference in my riding, and
why there is such a *big* difference between riding a bad horse
out of a chute where there's a band playing and folks cheer-
ing, and riding that same horse out where there's not a soul
for miles around. I seem to lose my confidence out here by
myself this way; and then riding along, not knowing just
when the horse is apt to go to bucking, sort of gets on my
nerve. I've come to find out that it sure ain't like riding that
horse in front of the grandstand. I *know* he's going to buck

there, and exactly when. I'm prepared for it, and when he's through, I'm through riding him too.

"You notice," he says after a while, "that I ride very different when inside of the corral than I do when out of it. . . . I guess that only goes to prove I'm a show hand, and not a cowboy. I followed circuses and Wild West shows as a kid, and learned to ride there. Afterward I took on contests, but I never rode a bucking horse outside of corrals or show grounds before. I don't have to tell you that I never rode outside of town limits either—you can see that; but it's sure surprising to me how much there's to contend with out here, not only with the kind of horses a feller rides, but the country is so doggone big, and there's so much a man has to know, to work in it and qualify."

We was saddling up as usual the next morning when we notice the stranger had picked his own horse. He tied a few belongings on the saddle and then turned toward us all as we was getting ready to file out for that day's riding.

"I'm not riding with the outfit today," he says, walking towards us and smiling. "And you boys won't have to look for me after the day's ride is over, 'cause I'm going back to where I can ride my bucking horse inside a fence, where there's people around to watch me, and a brass band playing and keeping time with my pony's hoofs as they hit the ground."

He started to get on his horse and ride away. We watched him the while and noticed what a change had come over the fancy rigging that'd been so pretty and shiny just a few days past. The neat boots was et up with alkali, the fancy stitching all unraveled, from the ramblings he'd done afoot. The saddle was all loose and tore apart here and there.

"The country sure put its mark on that outfit," says Joe

as we rode out of the corral. "Dang shame, too; it was sure pretty."

A month went by, and then one day Long Tom received a letter from the stranger; inside the envelope was a newspaper clipping and telling some of the winners of the prizes at some rodeo. Heading the list was a name underlined; the man packing that name had won first prize in the bucking horse contest and first in rope spinning also. At the bottom of the strip was handwriting which said: "The name underlined is your truly, *the stranger.*"

We all read the strip; after which Long Tom poured a little syrup on the back of it and pasted it to the wall. On the top of the strip, and to sort of decorate and identify, he nailed a twisted piece of silver which the brown horse had kicked off the stranger's saddle. It had been found that day out on the hardpan flat.

TWELFTH STORY

ON THE DODGE

I 'D HEARD A FEW shots the night before, and I had a
hunch they was being *exchanged;* but as the deer season
was open and the town dudes was out for 'em, I just
figgered maybe a couple of bucks had made their last jump,
and I let it go at that.

The next morning when I went to run in the ponies for
a fresh horse to do the day's riding on, I finds that my big
buckskin was missing, my own horse, and one of the best I
ever rode. I makes another circle of the pasture and comes
to a gate at one corner and stops. On the ground, plain as
you wanted to see, was boot marks where some hombre had
got off to open the gate and lead my buckskin through.

I sure knowed my horse's tracks when I saw 'em, 'cause in
shoeing him I'd always take care to round the shoe aplenty
so it'd protect the frog when running through the rocks. I'd
recognize that round hoofprint anywheres, and I wasn't apt
to forget the spike-heel boot mark, either.

I remembers the shots I'd heard, and I wondered if my
horse missing that way wasn't on account of somebody being

after somebody else and one of 'em needing a fresh horse right bad, just "borrowed" mine.

Well, I thinks he must of needed him worse than I did, and I sure give him credit for knowing a good horse when he sees one, but I wasn't going to part with my buckskin that easy.

I runs the other horses in the corral and snares me the best one the company had, opens the gate and straddles him on the jump. Out we go, him a-bucking and a-bawling and tearing down the brush. I didn't get no fun out of his actions that morning—I was in too big a hurry; and when I started to get rough, he lined out like the good horse he was.

I picks up the tracks of the horse thief out of the fence a ways, gets the lay of where he'd headed, and rides on like I was trying to head a bunch of mustangs. About a mile on his trail, I comes across a brown saddle horse looking like he'd been sat on fast and steady, and says to my own brown as we ride by like a comet: "Looks like that hombre sure did need a fresh horse."

I'm heading down a draw on a high lope, wondering why that feller in the lead never tried to cover his tracks, when I hear somebody holler, and so close that I figgered they must of heard me coming and laid for me. I had no choice when I was told to hold 'em up, and that I done.

My thirty-thirty was took away from me; then the whole bunch that I reckoned to be a posse, circled around and a couple searched me for a six-gun without luck. "Do you recognize that horse, any of you?" asked the one I took to be the sheriff. "Sure looks like the same one," answers a few, and one goes further to remark that my build and clothes sure tallies up with the description.

"Where do you come from and where was you headed in such a hurry?" asks the sheriff.

"I'm from the cow camp on Arrow Springs," I says, "and I'm headed on the trail of somebody who stole my horse last night." And riding ahead with half a dozen carbines pointed my way, I shows 'em the trail I was following. "Most likely one of our men," one of 'em says; and the sheriff backs him with, "Yes, we just let a man go awhile back."

"The hell you say!" I busts in, getting peeved at being held back that way. "Do you think you house-plants can tell

me anything about this track or any other tracks? What's more," I goes on, getting red in the face, "I can show you where I started following it, and where whoever stole my horse left his wore-out pony in the place of mine."

"Now, don't get rambunctious, young feller. Tracks is no evidence in court nohow, and if I'm lucky enough to get you there without you decorating a limb on the way, that's all I care. Where was you night before last?" he asks sudden.

"At the camp, cooking a pot of frijoles; and bedded there afterwards," I answers just as sudden.

"Fine for you so far, but is there anybody up at the camp who can prove you *was* there?"

"No, I'm there alone and keeping tab on a herd of dry stuff; but if you'll go to the home ranch, the foreman'll tell you how he hired me some two weeks back, if that'll do any good."

"I'm afraid it won't," he says. "That wouldn't prove anything on your whereabouts the time of the holdup. Your appearance and your horse are against you; you're a stranger in these parts, and the evidence points your way; and till your innocence is proved, I'll have to hold you on the charge of murder along with the robbery of the Torreon County Bank."

That jarred my thoughts a considerable, and it's quite a spell before I can round 'em to behave once more. The whole crowd is watching the effect of what the sheriff just said, and I don't aim to let 'em think I was rattled any. I showed about as much expression as a gambler and finally remarks:

"I reckon you ginks has got to get *somebody* for whatever's been pulled off, and it sure wouldn't look right to go back empty-handed, would it?" I says as I sized up the bunch.

A couple of the men are sent toward my camp to look for evidence, and two others start on the trail I was following, which leaves the sheriff and three men to escort me to town some sixty miles away.

I'm handcuffed; my reins are took away from me and one of the men is leading my horse. We travel along at a good gait, and I'm glad nobody's saying much; it gives me a chance to think, and right at that time I was making more use out of that think tank of mine than I thought I'd ever need to. I knowed I couldn't prove that I was at my camp the night of the holdup, and me being just a drifting cowboy happening to drop in the country at the wrong time, looked kinda bad for suspicious folks.

After sundown when we strike a fence and finally come to a ranch house, I was noticing a couple of the men was slopping all over their saddles and getting mighty tired; but I only had feelings for the tired horses that had to pack 'em. One of 'em suggests that they'd better call it a day and stop at the ranch for the night, and we rides in, me feeling worse than a trapped coyote.

I'm gawked at by all hands as we ride up; and I'm not at all pleased when I see one hombre in the family crowd that I do know, 'cause the last time I seen him, I'd caught him blotting the brand on a critter belonging to the company I was riding for and putting his own iron in the place of it. I was always kind of peaceable and kept it to myself, but between him and me, I offered to bet him that if he'd like to try it again I could puncture him and stand off five hundred yards while I was doing it. I'd never seen him since till now.

He gives me a kind of a mean look and I sees he's pleased to notice that I'm being took in for something. They hadn't heard of the holdup as yet, but it wasn't long till the news was spread.

Between bites of the bait that was laid before us, the sheriff took it onto hisself to tell all about it. I was interested to hear what was said, 'cause the details of the holdup was news to me too, and what was most serious was that the two masked bandits killed one man, and another wasn't expected to live; they'd got away with about ten thousand dollars. The women-folks sure kept a long ways from me after that.

The conversation was just about at its worst, for me, when the door opened and in walked a young lady, the prettiest young lady I remember ever seeing. All hands turned their heads her direction as she walked in, and the talk was checked for a spell.

"One of the family," I figgers as she makes her way to the other lady folks. I hears some low talk and feels accusing fingers pointing my way. In the meantime the sheriff and his men had cleared most everything that was fit to eat off the table; one of the ladies inquires if they'd like more, but none seemed to worry if *I* had my fill.

I glances where I figger the young lady to be, and instead of getting a scornful glance, as I'd expected, I finds a look in her eyes that's not at all convinced that I could of done all that was said; and a few minutes later there's more warm spuds and roast beef hazed over *my* shoulder, and I knowed the hand that done the hazing was none other than that same young lady's.

Arrangements was made for a room upstairs, and as the sheriff took the lead, me and the deputies following, I glanced at the girl once more, and as I went up the stairs I carried with me visions of a pretty face with a hint of a smile.

The three deputies unrolled a roundup bed that was furnished, and jumped in together; the sheriff and me took possession of a fancier bed with iron bedsteads. My wrist was handcuffed to his and we made ourselves comfortable as much as we could under the circumstances.

A lot of trouble was made, before the lamp was blowed out, to show there was no use me trying to get away.

In turning over, my fingers come acrost a little mohair rope I used for belt and emergency "piggin' string" (rope to tie down cattle). It was about six feet long, and soft.

The three deputies, after being in the cold all day and coming in a warm house tired and getting away with all that was on the table, was plumb helpless, and they soon slept and near raised the roof with the snoring they done.

The sheriff, having more responsibility, was kind of restless, but after what seemed a couple of hours he was also breathing like he never was going to wake up, leaving me a-thinking, and a-thinking.

The girl's face was in my mind through all what I thought; and the hint of her smile was like a spur a-driving me to prove that she was right in the stand she'd took. There was three reasons why I should get away and try to get the guilty parties; one was to get my good old buckskin back; another was to clear myself; but the main one, even though I didn't realize it sudden, was the girl.

If the guilty parties wasn't found, I knowed I'd most likely take the place of one of 'em. I just had to clear myself somehow, and the only way was to break loose to do it.

I was still fingering the piggin' string at my belt. I couldn't see the window and concludes it must be pitch-dark outside. A coyote howled, and the dogs barked an answer.

"Wonder if I can make it?" And something inside tells

me that I'd *better* make it, and now, or I'd never have another chance.

The sheriff acts kinda fidgety as I try to ease my piggin' string under his neck. I lays quiet awhile and tries it again, and about that time he turns over just right and lays over that string as though I'd asked him to. His turning over that way scared me, so that I didn't dare move for a spell; but finally I reach over and grab the end of the string that was sticking out on the other side, makes a slip knot and puts the other end of the string around a steel rod of the bedstead; and still hanging on to that end, I'm ready for action.

From then on, I don't keep things waiting. With my handcuffed arm, I get a short hold on the string; and with my free arm, I gets a lock on the sheriff's other arm all at once. That sure wakes him up, but he can't holler or budge, and the more he pulls with the arm that's handcuffed to mine, the more that string around his neck is choking him. I whispers in his ear to tell me where I can get the keys for the handcuffs before I hang him to dry, and by listening close I hears: "In my money belt."

I had to let go of his arm to get that key, but before he had time to do anything, my fist connected with the point of his chin in a way that sure left him limp. I takes the handcuffs off my wrist, turns the sheriff over on his stomach and relocks the handcuffs with his arms back of him, stuffs a piece of blanket in his mouth, and cutting the piggin' string in two, ties the muffler in place and uses the other piece to anchor his feet together.

The three deputies on the floor was still snoring away and plumb innocent of what was going on. I sneaks over to where I'd seen 'em lay my rifle, picks out an extra six-shooter out of the holster of one of the sleeping men, and heads to where I thought the window to be.

It was locked from the inside with a stick, and removing that, I raised it easy; and still easier I starts sliding out of the window and down as far as my arms lets me, and lets go.

I picks myself up in a bunch of dry weeds and heads for the corrals for anything I could find to ride. I'm making record time on the way and pretty near bumps into—somebody.

My borrowed six-shooter is pointed right at that somebody sort of natural, and before I can think—

"Don't shoot, cowboy," says a soft voice. "I knowed you'd come, and I been waiting for you. I got the best horse in the country saddled and ready, and if you can ride him, nothing can catch you."

I recognized the young lady; she came closer as she spoke and touched my arm.

"Follow me," she says, pulling on my shirt sleeve, and the tinkle of her spurs and the swish of her riding skirt sounded like so much mighty fine music as I trotted along.

But there was sounds of a commotion at the house. Either the weeds had give me away or the sheriff come out of it. Anyway, a couple of lights was running through the house, doors was slamming, and pretty soon somebody fires a shot.

"Them folks sure have learnt to miss me quick," I remarks as we push open the corral gate. Then I'm up to the snorting pony in two jumps. I see he's hobbled and tied ready to fork; and sticking my rifle through the rosadero, I takes the hobbles off of him, lets him break away with me a-hanging to his side and I mounts him flat-footed as he goes through the gate.

I was making a double getaway, one from the sheriff and

the other from the girl. I knowed, the way I felt, it would have seemed mighty insulting for me to try and thank her with little words. I wanted to let her know somehow that *if* she ever wished to see me break my neck, I'd do it *for her,* and with a smile.

"I sure thank you," I says as I passes her (which goes to prove that there's times when a feller often says things he wants to say least), but I had to say something.

The whole outfit was coming from the house. There was a couple more shots fired, and with the noise of the shots, my old pony forgot to take time to buck and lined out like a scared rabbit, me a-helping him all I could. We hit a barb-wire fence and went through it like them wires was threads, and went down the draw, over washouts and across creeks like it was all level country.

The old pony was stampeding, and it was the first time in my life that I wanted a ride of that kind to last, and being that we was going the direction I wanted to go, I couldn't get there any too fast to suit me.

I'm quite a few miles away from the ranch when I decides I'd better pull up my horse if I wanted to keep him under me after daybreak, and that I did, but I managed to keep him at a stiff trot till a good twenty-five miles was between us and where we'd left.

Daybreak catches up with us a few miles farther on, and I figgers I'd better stop awhile to let the pony feed and water. I takes a look over the way I just come, and being that I'm halfways up a mountain, I gets a good view of the valley, and if anybody is on my trail, I'd sure get to see 'em first and at a good ten miles away.

The little old pony buckles up and tries to kick me as I gets off, and not satisfied with that, takes a run on the hackamore rope and tries to jerk away, but his kind of horse-flesh was nothing new to me, and in a short while he was behaving and eating as though he knowed it was the best thing for him to do.

A good horse always did interest me, and as I'm off a ways studying his eleven hundred pounds' worth of good points, I notices a sackful of something tied on the back of the saddle. "Wonder what it can be," I thinks out aloud as I eases up to the horse and unties it. I opens the sack, and finds all that's necessary to the staff of life when traveling light and fast the way I was. There was "jerky" and rice, salt and coffee, with a big tin plate and cup throwed in to cook and eat it out of.

"Daggone her little hide!" I says, grinning and a-trying to appreciate the girl's thoughtfulness. "Who'd ever thought it?"

I cooked me a bait in no time, and getting around on the outside of it, am able to appreciate life, freedom and a good horse once again. And wanting to keep all that, I don't forget that these hills are full of posse-men, and that the other bunch at the ranch would soon be showing themselves on my trail. There was what I took to be a small whirlwind down on the flat. If it was a dust made by the posse they'd sure made good time considering the short stretch of daylight they'd had to do any tracking by.

I takes another peek out on the flat before cinching up, and sure enough there was little objects bobbing up and down under that dust.

I had the lead on 'em by ten miles, and I knowed if I could get on my horse and was able to stick him, that I'd soon lose 'em but doing that away from the corral sure struck me as a two-man's job. What I was afraid of most was him getting away from me; his neck was as hard to bend as a pine tree, and his jaw was like iron, but I had to get action, and mighty quick, 'cause the distance between me and them was getting shorter every minute.

It helped a lot that I'd hobbled him before he was rested up from the ride I'd give him that night, and taking the rope off the saddle, I passes one end of it through the hobble and tied it. About then the old pony lets out a snort and he passes me like a blue streak. I just has time to straighten up, give a flip to the rope that was running through my hands, follow it a couple of jumps and get set.

My heels was buried out of sight when the stampeding pony hits the end and the rope tightens up; he made a big jump in the air and as his front feet are jerked out from under him, he lands in a heap and makes the old saddle pop. I follows the rope up to him, keeping it tight so's he can't get his feet back under him, and before he knows it I've got him tied down solid.

I takes a needed long breath and looks out on the flat once more; there's no time to waste, that I can see; them little dark objects of awhile ago had growed a heap bigger and was a-bobbing up and down faster than ever. I straightens up my stirrups, gets as much of the saddle under me as I can, and twists the pony's head so's to hold him down till I'm ready to let him up, and starts to take the rope off his feet.

He knows it the minute he's free, and is up like a shot; he keeps on getting up till I can near see the angels, and when he hit the earth again he lit a-running—and straight toward the posse and the ranch.

I tries to haze and turn him with my hat, but he'd just duck out from under it and go on the same way. So far he didn't act as though he wanted to take the time to buck with me, and I'd been glad of it, but now, we just had to come to a turning point and the only way I seen was to scratch it out of him.

Screwing down on my saddle as tight as I could, I brings one of my ten-point "hooks" right up along his neck far as I could reach and drags it back. That sure stirred up the dynamite in him of a sudden, and I had a feeling that the cantle of my saddle was a fast mail train and I was on the track; but he turned, and as luck would have it I was still with him. He kept on a-turning and all mixed in with his sunfishing and side-winding sure made it a puzzle to tell which was heads or tails.

What worried me most was the fear of being set afoot, and I'd been putting up a *safe* ride on that account, but that old pony wasn't giving me a fair deal. He fought his head too much, and I was getting tired of his fooling. I reaches down, gets a shorter holt on the hackamore rope and lets him have it, both rowels a-working steady—and two wildcats tied by the tail and throwed across the saddle couldn't of done any more harm.

We sure made a dust of our own out there on the side of that mountain, and I'd enjoyed the fight more if things had of been normal, but they wasn't, and I had the most to lose. The little horse finally realized that, the way I went at him, 'cause pretty soon his bucking got down to crowhopping and gradually settled down to a long run up the slope of the mountain. That young lady was sure right when she said that if I could ride him, nothing could catch me.

He was pretty well winded when we got to the top, but I could see he was a long ways from tired, and letting him jog along easy we started down into a deep canyon.

My mind is set on tracking down the feller what stole my buckskin horse, and I figgers the way I'm heading I'll sometime come across his trail, but I'd like mighty well to shake loose from that bunch chasing me before I get much farther; and thinking strong on that, I spots a bunch of mustangs a mile or so to my left, and there was my chance to leave a mighty confusing trail for them that was following.

I sneak up out of sight and above the "fuzztails," and when I am a few hundred yards off, I shows up sudden over a ridge and heads their way. I lets out a full-grown war whoop as I rides down on 'em, and it sure don't take the wild ones long to make distance from that spot.

My horse being barefooted and his hoofs wore smooth, his tracks blend in natural with that of the mustangs, and I keeps him right in the thick of 'em. The wild ones make a half circle which takes me out of my way some, but I'm satisfied to follow, seeing that it also takes me on the outskirts of where I figgered some of the posse outfit might be.

My horse was ganting up and getting tired, but them wild ponies ahead kept him wanting to catch up; and me holding him down to a steady long lope made him all the more anxious to get there with 'em. I was wishing I could stop to let him feed and rest awhile, but I didn't dare to just yet; my trail wasn't covered up well enough.

The sun is still an hour high when the wild ones I was following came out of the junipers and lined out across a little valley. I figgers I'm a good seventy-five miles from where I made my getaway, and even though my horse hates to have the mustangs leave him behind, he's finally willing to slow down to a walk. I rubs his sweaty neck and tells him what a good horse he is, and for the first time I notice his ears are in a slant that don't show meanness.

The wild ones run ahead and plumb out of sight; the sun had gone over the hill, and it was getting dark, and on the back trail I don't see no sign of any posse. Still following the trail the mustangs had left, I begins to look for a place where I can branch off, and coming acrost a good-sized creek I turns my horse up it into the mountains.

"Old pony," I says to my horse as we're going along in the middle of the stream, "if that posse is within twenty miles of us, they're sure well mounted; and what's more," I goes on, "if they can tell our tracks from all the fresh tracks we've left scattered through the country behind, in front and all directions, why, they can do a heap more than any human I know of."

I'm a couple of miles up the mountain and still following the stream, when a good grassy spot decides me to make camp. The little horse only flinches as I get off this time, and he don't offer to jerk away. I pulls the saddle off, washes his back with cool water and hobbles him on the tall grass, where he acts plumb contented to stay and feed.

Clouds are piling up over the mountain; it's getting cold and feels like winter coming on. I builds me a small Injun fire, cooks me up a bait, and rolling a smoke, stretches out.

"Some girl," I caught myself saying as I throwed my dead cigarette away. . . . The little horse rolled out a snort the same as to say, "All is well," and pretty soon I'm not of the world no more.

It's daylight when a daggone magpie hollers out and makes me set up, and I wonders as I stirs up the coffee what's on the program for today. My horse acts real docile as I saddles him up; he remembers when I gives his neck a rub that it pays to be good.

I crosses on one side of a mountain pass and on over a

couple of ridges and down into another valley of white sage and hardpan. I don't feel it safe to come out in the open and cross that valley, so I keeps to the edge close to the foothills and junipers.

My horse, picking his way on the rocky trail, jars a boulder loose and starts it down to another bigger boulder that's just waiting for that much of an excuse to start rolling down to the bottom of the canyon; a good many more joins in, and a noise echoes up that can be heard a long ways.

As the noise of the slide dies down, I hears a horse nicker, and it sounds not over five hundred yards away. I didn't give my horse a chance to answer, and a hunch makes me spur up out of the canyon and over the ridge. I was afraid of the dust I'd made in getting over the ridge.

I'm splitting the breeze down a draw; and looking back over my shoulder, I'm just in time to get the surprise of my life. A whole string of riders are topping the ridge I'd just went over, and here they come heading down on me hell-bent for election. I know it's them, and I know they seen my dust; and worse yet, I know they're on fresh horses.

"Now," I asks the scenery, "how in Sam Hill do you reckon for them to be in this perticular country, and so quick?" And the only answer I could make out was that when I struck the mustangs and put too many marks in front of 'em for 'em to follow, they just trusted to luck and cut acrost to where they thought I'd be heading.

My only way out is speed, and my pony is giving me all he can of that; but it's beginning to tell on him, and I don't like the way he hits the other side of the washouts we come acrost.

A bullet creases the bark off a piñon not far to my right; another raises the dust closer, and even though I sure hated to, I had to start using the spurs. The little horse does his final best, and I begins to notice that the bullets are falling short, and it ain't long when I'm out of range of 'em.

"Old-timer," I says to my tired horse as we're drifting along, "if you only had a few hours' rest, we'd sure make them hombres back of us wonder how thin air could swallow us so quick."

We tops a rise in the foothills, and ahead of us is a bunch of mustangs. They evaporate quick, leaving a big cloud of dust. They can't do me any good this time; my horse is too far gone; but I thinks of another way and proceeds to act.

I reaches over, takes the hackamore off my horse's head and begins to loosen the latigo. My pony's took heart to keep up the speed awhile longer, on account of them wild ones ahead and wanted to catch up with 'em.

My saddle cinch is loose and a-flapping to one side; my chance comes as we go through a thick patch of buckbrush, and I takes advantage of it. I slides off my horse and takes my saddle with me; the old pony has nothing on him but the sweat where my saddle'd been. There's mustangs ahead, and with a snort and a shake of his tail he bids me good-by and disappears.

About that time me and my "riggin'" ain't to be seen no more, and when the posse rides by on the trail my horse'd left, there was a big granite boulder and plenty of buckbrush to keep me hid, and looking straight ahead for a dust, the sheriff and his three men kept right on a-going.

But I figgered they'd be back, sometime, and thinks I'd better be a-moving. I hangs my saddle up a piñon tree, leaves most of the grub with it, and, tearing up the gunnysack that was around it, proceeds to pad up my feet so they'd leave as little track as possible. Then I picks up my rifle and heads up towards a high point on the mountain where I could get the lay of the country.

I'm on what seems to be a high rocky ledge, and looking around for some shelter in it from the cold wind, and where I can hole up for the night. I comes to the edge of *nothing* —and stops short!

Another step, and I'd went down about three hundred feet; a fire at the bottom of it showed me how deep it was, and by that fire was two men; maybe they're deer-hunters, I thinks. I keeps a-sizing up the outfit, and then I spots three hobbled ponies feeding to one side a ways, and there amongst 'em was my good old buckskin. I'd recognize his two white front feet and his bald face anywheres.

I'm doing some tall figgering by then, and I has a hunch that before daybreak I'll be well mounted again and on my own horse. Seeing that my rifle was in good working order, I slides down off my perch to where going down is easier and surer of a foothold. I'm down about halfways, and peeking through a buckbrush, I gets a better look at them two hombres by the fire. The more I size 'em up, the surer I gets of my suspicions.

I'm close enough to see that one of the men is about my built, and not only that, but it looks like he had on my clothes. The other man I couldn't make much out of—he was laying down on his face as though he was asleep; but I could see he was some stouter and shorter.

Well, all appearances looked a safe bet to me, and beating my own shadow for being noiseless, I gets to within a hundred feet of 'em.

"Stick 'em up," I says quiet and steady for fear of their nerves being on edge and stampeding with 'em. One of 'em flinches some but finally reaches for the sky, the other that's laying down don't move, and I warns him that playing possum don't go with me; but threatening didn't do no good there. I'm told that he's wounded and out of his head—I remember the sheriff saying that one of the men had been wounded, which altogether tallied up fine as these being the men *me* and the sheriff wanted.

"Take his hands away from his belt and stretch 'em out where I can see 'em then," I says, not wanting to take the chance. That done, I walks over toward 'em and stops, keeping the fire between. I notice that the man laying has no gun on or near him; the other feller with his arms still up is packing two of 'em, and I makes him shed them by telling him to unbuckle his cartridge belt.

I backs him off at the point of my rifle and goes to reaching for the dropped belt and six-guns, when from behind and too close for comfort somebody sings out for me to drop my rifle and reach for the clouds. I does that plenty quick, and looking straight ahead like I'm told to, I sees a grin spreading all over the face of the man I'd just held up a minute ago.

"Where does this third party come in?" thinks I. My six-shooter is jerked out of my belt as I try to figger a way out, and is throwed out of reach along with my rifle; and then of a sudden the light of the fire in front of me was snuffed out, and with a sinking feeling all went dark. . . .

When I come to again, I hear somebody groaning, and I tries to get my think tank working; my head feels about the size of a washtub, and sore. Whatever that hombre hit me with sure wasn't no feather pillow. I tries to raise a hand and finds they're both tied; so is my feet, and about all I can move is my eyelashes. Things come back to me gradual, and star-gazing at the sky I notice it's getting daybreak.

Hearing another groan, I manages to turn my head enough to see the same hombre that'd been laying there that night and in the same position. I hears the other two talking, off a ways. It sounds by the squeak of saddle leather that they're getting ready to move, and that sure wakes me up to action.

I know I can't afford to let 'em get away, and I sure won't. Raising up far as I can, I hollers for one of 'em to come over a minute. There's some cussing heard, but soon enough here comes the tallest one, and he don't no more than come near me when I asks him to give me a chance to loosen up my right boot, that my sprained ankle was bothering me terrible.

"You needn't think you can pull anything over on me," he says sarcastic. He sizes my boot up awhile and then remarks: "But I'll let you pull 'em both off. I need a new pair."

My arms and feet are free, but awful stiff; he's standing off a few feet, and with rifle ready for action is watching me like a hawk while I'm fidgeting around with my right boot; I gets my right hand inside of it as though to feel my ankle, but what I was feeling for mostly was a gun I'd strapped in there.

(When I started out on the trail of my buckskin I figgered on getting him; I also figgered on running acrost somebody riding him that'd be a gunman, and I'd prepared to compete with all the tricks of the gun-toter. This gun in my boot was what I called *my hole card*.)

My foot is up and toward him, and I'm putting on a lot of acting while getting hold of the handle and pulling back the hammer, but I manages that easy enough and squeezing my finger towards the trigger, I pulls.

That shot paralyzed him, and down he come. He'd no more than hit the ground when I falls on the rifle he'd dropped, and I starts pumping lead the direction of the other feller. His left arm was bandaged and tied up, but he was sure using his right so that our shots was passing one another halfways and regular. . . . Then I felt a pain in my left shoulder. I begins to get groggy—and pretty soon all is quiet once more.

I must of been disconnected from my thoughts for quite a spell, 'cause when I come to, this time the sun is way high. I straightens up to look around and recollect things, and it all came back some as I gets a glimpse of my buckskin feeding off a ways.

My shoulder's stiff and sore, but feeling around for the harm the bullet has done, I finds I'd just been creased, and being weak on account of not having anything under my belt either in the line of grub or moisture for the last twenty-four hours, that bullet was enough to knock me out.

I'm hankering for a drink right bad and starts looking for it on all fours, when in my rambling, I comes across a shadow, and looking right hard I can make out horse's hoofs, then his legs and on up to a party sitting on top of him and looking down at me. The warm sun had made me weak again, and I quits right there.

Somebody's pouring cool water down me, and when I opens my eyes again, I feels better control of 'em. I'm asked when I et last and I can't seem to remember; then I gets a vision of a pot of coffee, and flapjacks, smells frying bacon, and the dream that I'm eating evaporates with the last bite.

"Well, I see you found your buckskin," says a voice right close, and recognizing that voice makes me take notice of things. It was the sheriff's; the posse'd rode in on me.

"And by the signs around here," the same voice goes on, "it looks like you just got here in time and had to do a heap of shooting in order to get him, but I'm sure glad to see you did, 'cause along with that horse you got the two men we wanted for the robbery, which makes you free to go. No mistake this time."

That last remark brought real life to me, and interested again, I takes a look around. The two men was setting against a rock looking mighty weak and shot up. I looks for the third, and I'm told that he was being took in to the nearest ranch for care he was needing mighty bad.

"How does he come to be with these hombres?" I asks.

"He's a government service man out after these two outlaws," says the sheriff, "and your dropping in when you did is all that saved him—if we hadn't heard your shot, we'd never found this hole, and he'd been left to feed the buzzards."

Not wanting to hog all the credit, I says: "I've sure got to hand it to you too—for camping on a feller's trail the way you do it wasn't at all comfortable."

"Neither is a piggin' string around a feller's neck," comes back the sheriff, smiling.

It's after sundown as I tops a ridge and stops my buckskin. Out across a big sage and hardpan flat is a dust stirred up by the posse and their prisoners. I watches it a spell, and starting down the other side of the ridge, I remarks: "Buck, old horse, I'm glad you and me are naturally peaceable, 'cause being that way not only saves us from a lot of hard traveling, but it's a heap easier on a feller's think tank."

THIRTEENTH STORY

CATTLE RUSTLERS

T O MY WAY of thinking anybody with a lot of nerve
is never real bad all the way, wether he be a cattle
thief, or cattle rustler—the excitement he gets out
out of it is what he likes most, and you can bet your boots
that even tho he may be dealing from the bottom of the deck,
he's taking his from them what won't suffer from the loss,
or maybe even miss it; you're plumb safe when that kind
rides up to your camp to leave your silver mounted spurs
and bits scattered around as usual, and most likely if he sees
you're in need of a fresh horse he'll be real liberal in offer-
ing you the pick of his string—only danger is, if you're caught
riding one of them ponies, it may be kind of hard to explain just how you come in possession of said animal.

There's cases where some cowboy what's kind of reckless
and sorta free with his rope might get a heap worse reputation than what he deserves; and he gradually gets the blame
for any stock disappearing within a couple of hundred miles
from his stomping ground. Naturally that gets pretty deep

under his hide, with the result that he figgers he might just as well live up to his reputation, 'cause if he gets caught "going south" with five hundred head, he won't get hung any higher than he would for running off with just some old "ring-boned" saddle horse. Consequences is when the stock associations and others start to keep him on the move, he's using his *long rope* for fair, and when's he's moving there's a few carloads of prime stock making tracks ahead of him. In Wyoming a few of the feud men tried to even scores that way; the hillbilly was on horseback and toting a hair-trigger carbine.

I don't want to give the impression that the cattlemen started in the cow business by rustling, not by a long shot—they're plumb against it in all ways, and most of 'em would let their herd dwindle down to none rather than brand anything less'n they're sure it's their own. But there is some what naturally hates to see anything go unbranded wether it's theirs or not, and being the critter don't look just right to 'em without said iron, they're most apt to plant one on and sometimes the brand don't always fit.

Like, for instance, there was Bob Ryan riding mean horses all day and a lot of the night in all kinds of weather for somebody else at thirty a month and bacon. It wasn't any too interesting to him; he kinda hankered for a little range and a few head of stock of his own, and come to figgering that some outfits he'd rode for had no objections to their riders picking up a "slick" whenever it was safe. There was no reason much why them slicks couldn't just as well bear his own "iron" and that certain "ranny," being overambitious that way and sorta carefree, buys a few head of cows, calves, and yearlings, wherever he can get 'em and takes a "squatter" in the foothills, his weaning corrals being well hid higher up

in some heavy-timbered box canyon, and proceeds to drag a loop that makes him ashamed, at first.

There's the start of your cattle rustler—it's up to how wise he is, or how lucky, wether he keeps it up till he's really one or not. If he can get by till his herd is the size he wants it without getting caught, most likely he'll stop there and no one will know the difference, but if some inquisitive rider gets wind of his doings, and that wind scatters till it begins to look like a tornado, why, it's liable to leave him in bad humor and make him somewhat more reckless.

A few months after Bob started on his own, a couple of riders out on circle was bringing in a bunch to the "cutting grounds," and in the "drag" noticed four cows with big bags bellering their heads off—and no calves. In another drive there's two more. Next morning, the range boss takes two riders with him, leaving the straw boss take the others out on first circle—the six cows with the full bags was turned loose the night before and the boss finds 'em by a little corral in the brush still bellering (a cow and calf, if separated and losing track of one another, always return to where they'd last been together and wait for days till the one missing returns). There'd been a lot of cattle there and 'most impossible to track any special critter, so he goes up on a ridge toward the high mountains and "cuts" for tracks. A few miles to the north he runs across what he's looking for, and by the signs to be seen they sure must of been traveling and a horse track was there on top of the rest, looked a few days old.

Up a canyon it leads a ten or twelve miles, and they pass by Bob's camp, not seeing it. It was well hid and what's more, tracks is what the boss and the two riders was keeping their eyes on most—up a little further there's a corral and if it wasn't for them tracks it'd never be found. There'd been cattle there the night before, it was plain to see. They kept quiet and listened. Off into the timber higher up a calf was heard and single file they climbed towards where it sounded to be from. When figgering they was close enough, they scattered and went three ways and on past around where the cattle was feeding till they got up above 'em, then joined one another; and getting off their horses they climbed a high point, squatted, took their hats off, and looking thru the cracks of a red rock, they could see a few of the cattle below 'em. Bob had 'em on feed and under cover during the day and in the corral at night till the brands healed. Nothing of *him* could be seen anywheres, but he was there keeping his eye on what he could see of the back-trail and at the same time standing "day herd" on the cattle.

Bob knew 'most anyone would ride right up into the cattle, if in case they was looking for him figgering he'd be there, but he would of fooled 'em by just dropping off his perch into the other canyon and making distance—by the time they'd got thru looking for him he'd been in the next county. The boss reckoned on all that, being quite a hand on them sorta tricks himself at one time; so calculates the best thing to do is keep out of sight, circle around back to the corral, hide and wait till Bob brought the cattle down and put up the poles at the gate. Along about sundown, the cattle is coming and Bob is with 'em, drives 'em into the corral, and he's putting up the last pole when from three different places at close distance he hears the command "Put up your hands," " 'Way up there!" Bob reaches for the sky, knowing better than try to do different.

The next morning to the boss's surprise, there's no weaners in that corral; all grown stock mostly cows, and calves too young to be branded, but them cows had fresh irons and earmarks on 'em just beginning to heal. What was the original iron on them critters nobody could make out, it was blotched so bad and the ears cut so short that there was nothing to be seen but the *new iron*, that being sure visible and stretching from shoulder to hip-bone.

It was plain to see what Bob had been doing, but he had cattle of his own bearing the same iron, and he could prove it was of the first branding, and them weaners disappearing was a puzzle. The boss had a strong hunch he had 'em hid somewheres, but where? And how could he prove Bob did it?

Bob not being caught red-handed just lands into court and with his lawyer wins the fight; the judge and jury pronounces him "Not Guilty," and the lawyer takes the cattle for the fee. (It's 'most impossible to convict anyone of cattle rustling, and that's why "necktie parties" was so popular.) When the sun shines on his freedom again, the first thing that stares him in the eye is cattle once more, cattle everywhere on the hillsides and brakes—he knows it's his move, so calculates to make the most of it while moving. His idea is to clear enough to get him started in some new country, where he ain't branded so well.

He knows he'll get the blame for all that disappears in that territory, so he goes to work and takes pains to let everybody know in the town and country that he's hitting the breeze. He wants to let 'em understand that there'll be a whole state, maybe two, between him and those what suspicions. He sticks around for a week or more, straightening out his affairs, and the while telling the folks about him what a paradise this new country is where he's going to, that he wouldn't come back again on a bet.

The stage-driver takes him and his "thirty years' gathering" to the railroad station and comes back telling the storekeeper and livery-stable man that he's went for sure. He'd seen him buy a ticket for some town a thousand miles away, and everybody kinda draws a long breath saying something like "good riddance of bad rubbish."

Sure enough, Bob had went all right, and arrives at this new country unknown and walking kinda straight. The sheriff ain't ever heard of him and he inquires 'round at the stable where the headquarters for the Blue River Land and Cattle Company might be found. The superintendent, upon his asking for a job, informs him that he's full-handed excepting that he could use a good man "snapping broncs."

A few days later you could see Bob inside the breaking corral of the home ranch; four broncs are tied up and getting "eddicated" and another's saddled ready to be "topped off." He's standing there rolling a smoke, his mind not at all on the hobbled glass-eyed horse standing alongside him with legs wide apart and tipping the saddle near straight up with the hump that makes the boys ride. His eyes are on over and past the other broncs tied to the corral, and sees only away across the valley some fifteen miles. Timber out there draws his attention, and Bob wonders what the range is like at the perticular spot.

It's quite a ride for a green bronc, but not many days later you could see him winding up, following the cow trails to that timber and water hole. He passes two "alkali licks" and rides on thru the aspens to the mesa—white sage, grama, and mountain bunch grass everywhere, shad scale on the flat and wild peas in the gullies higher up. There's a line of troughs at the water hole and a few head of the Blue River cattle are watering there.

That night at the bunkhouse with the boys, Bob hazes the talk to drifting on about the springs and holdings of the company and by just listening, asking no questions, he finds that the little range he'd rode into that day was held by the outfit. He had a hunch they was holding it with no rights, and everyone in the country had took it for granted it was theirs, never bothering about finding out.

A few months later the broncs are all "snapped out," a pay-check in Bob's chap pocket, and then pretty soon a log house is up and smoke coming out of the fireplace thru the timber where the line of troughs and alkali licks was located. There was a howl from the company about somebody "jumping" one of their springs, but that don't do no good; saying they owned that range and proving it was two different things; and Bob stayed on, taking in horses to break at ten dollars a head and making a big bluff as to how much he's putting away, every so often.

One day Bob disappears and is gone for 'most six weeks; his place being out of the way of any riders, nobody knows he'd went or returned, and if you'd asked him where he was keeping himself he'd said, "home." Anyway, in a few days

after his return, he buys a hundred head of mixed stock, and some kinda wondered where he'd got the money to buy stock with, figgering even if he did make a good stake at breaking horses, it wouldn't buy one-fourth the cattle he'd paid cash for. He disappears once more without anyone knowing of it and buys another little bunch of "dogies." Bob was getting bolder every time and the big outfits a thousand miles to the north and east was putting out a big reward for a cattle thief they didn't have the description of. They'd plumb forgot about Bob, knowing him to be south somewhere and doing well, as they'd hear tell from the riders traveling thru.

He got so he could change a brand on a critter, and with a broken blade and a little acid of his own preparation make that brand to suit his taste, and in fifteen minutes appear like it'd been there since the critter was born. You could feel the scaly ridge in the hide where the iron was supposed to've been and even a little white hair here and there; it would sure stand inspection from either the eye or the hand.

Bob knowing every hill, coulee, flat, creek, and river of that country, was a great help to him. He'd rode every foot of it for a hundred miles around. It was where he'd stood trial and lost his first herd. He knew the folks there had forgot him and that's what he wanted. It left him a clear trail out of suspicion; the train would take and leave him at some neighboring town. At night getting a couple of ponies and hitting out on "jerky," a little flour, and salt before sun up, he'd skirt the foothills and never would a rider get sight of him. Laying low by day and riding by night he'd locate the herds with the best beef and camp within a few miles of 'em so if they drifted he'd know their whereabouts and, soon as the weather permit, fog on behind 'em.

At the first sign of a strong wind, when tracks a few hours

old are sifted over with fine sand, or before a first snow, you could see Bob getting his "piggin' string," unlimbering his ropes and testing his acid; his copper "running iron" was always with him too, hid between his saddle skirting and the lining; his 30–30 well cleaned and oiled and the old smoke wagon under his shirt and resting on his chap belt, he'd hit out on the best horse the country had for the herd he'd been watching, and go to cutting out a couple of carloads of the primest stuff he could get. Of course, by the time he'd get 'em to the shipping point, or market, they'd only be "feeders," but that brought a fair price.

The first night he'd camp on the critters' tails till they'd use all the energy they had to get out of the way. (In some cases it's been known of some cattle rustlers covering over forty miles single-handed with fifty some odd head in one night.) Bob had figgered a long time ahead the best way to take his cattle out, the hiding places for the day, and water to go with it, keeping shy of fences and ranches. At first sign of the rising sun his cattle was watered and taken up in some timbered canyon, the brands was worked over and a few hours later the herd was bedded down or feeding. The next night would be easier on both man and stock, and by the third, Bob felt pretty secure, but never would you find him with the cattle during the day. The cattle being too tired to stray away was left soon as watered and taken on feed. When they'd be hid, Bob would "back-trail" a mile or so, where he could watch his cattle and see any riders what might be following him. In case there was, he had plenty of time before they got to his cattle and had 'em identified to make a getaway; for even tho an "iron" may be worked over into another, the rustler ain't going to take a chance. There may be a "marker" in that bunch that only the owner, or the riders familiar with the cattle, would recognize; and that's enough to entitle the rustler to the stout limb and a piece of rope if he's caught.

When once out of the stolen cattle's territory and a hundred miles or so farther the cattle are loaded into the cars. (It's done at night if there is no inspection in that particular state.) Bob's going to stick to the finish 'cause he figgers his iron is going to stand the inspection of the stockyards inspector—he can show you where that brand is recorded and that they're his cattle unless you have reason to be real out of the ordinary inquisitive and want to know too much—but even then Bob has cattle bearing the same "iron" on his range to the south, and it may be mighty hard to prove they're not his. Furthermore, nobody knows or can prove he's been out of the country or whether he's shipped some of his own cattle or not—and no one had seen him around where the cattle was stolen.

It was getting real interesting, and he did not realize that he was taking a liking to stealing cattle and making clean getaways. The herd at his home camp was getting to be just a bluff, bearing half a dozen different recorded irons and earmarks. He was beginning to use them to fall back on in case investigation was made and traced back to his "hangout." He'd made three trips to Chicago and was just thinking of settling down to steal no more. He knew this good luck wouldn't last, and besides, picking up a few "orejanas" now and again around his own little range to the south might prove just as interesting; but the fever had him, with the result that he found out no matter how close you figger there's always something you'll overlook what'll give you away.

He started north for another raid, and thought he'd take

his own saddle horses along this time, being that good horses are hard to pick up everywhere that way. There was one horse especially he hated to leave behind. It was a big blood bay, bald-faced and stocking-legged, and when he got to his destination to the north, and the stock car was being switched at the yards, one of the old-timers recognized the horse and kept mum till Bob came to the stock car and led him out with his other horse. Ten minutes later Bob was feeding up at the "open-all-night" restaurant and watching the front door. The sheriff comes thru the kitchen and when Bob turned around to his "ham and eggs" there was the muzzle of a .45 staring him in the eye.

He lost his second herd to the same lawyer and faced the same judge of two years before. He'd only stole one horse where he'd got away with over two hundred head of cattle in that country, but that one horse put the kibosh on him. There was no proof that he'd stole any cattle, but they suspicioned mighty strong; and they couldn't of handed him any more if they could of proved it. So figgering on killing two birds with one stone, the judge, not weeping any, throws the book at him, which means he gives Bob the limit.

If Bob would of had better luck the first time he tried to settle down in the country where he'd made such a bad "reputation" for himself, most likely by now he'd been just a prosperous cowman and kept his "long ropes" to home. I don't figger Bob was bad, just a little too anxious to have something, and later on getting too much satisfaction in outwitting others. Any stranger was welcome to Bob's camp to feed and rest up; a fresh horse, or anything else he had, was offered to them what needed it, and it wouldn't matter if your pack horse was loaded with gold nuggets they was just as safe in his bunkhouse, or maybe safer, than in the safety vault. His specialty was cattle and he got to love to use his skill in changing irons.

He was just like a big average of the western outlaw and cattle rustler; his squareness in some things made up for his crookedness in others. There was no petty work done: saddle, spurs, and chaps was safe hanging over the corral, but there was one thing you had to keep away from in the rustler's doings; if you saw at a distance a smoke going up, one man with a critter down and a horse standing rope's length away, it's always a good idea to ride 'way around and keep out of sight, unless you want your Stetson perforated.

FOR THE SAKE OF FREEDOM

I WAS HEADED FOR wild horse country. I'd just ended up on a job of breaking a string of fine three and four year old colts for the Kant-Hook / horse out-fit, drawed my money, run in my private 𝄞 horses and was catering to my natural hankering to drift on and see new territory.

I'd often heard tell of a country a few hundred miles to the south, where there was not much else but wild horses and antelope, and some few cattle. It was a desert country, water miles apart, some of the springs was poisonous and many others dried up during summer months. On account of the land being covered with sharp lava and shale rock it was mighty hard on hoofs. Brush feed and scarce grama grass was like on the run, and the few cattle that ranged in that country kept sore-footed and poor by trying to catch up with it, and after a day and a night of rustling for feed, with very little rest in between, they'd hardly get their fill or rest when thirst would force them to hightail to the closest watering place, which would be many miles away.

That was what I'd heard tell of that country, the wild horse country I was heading for. I'd been in many countries like it before and liked 'em well; there was lots of room and no fences and a feller appreciated shade and water more. It wasn't no cow country, and most of the cattle that run in there had just strayed and got to ranging there of their own accord. They'd be rounded up once or twice a year and then left free to range as they wished. It was open country all around and many of 'em would drift back.

But if that perticular country wasn't much fit for cattle the wild horse seemed to do well enough and accumulated there, and being they was on range where there was so few cattle, not many riders come to spoil their peace. Only once in a long while mustang runners would set up a water or blind trap and a few of the wild ones would be caught and shipped out of the territory. But the wild ones kept pretty well up to their numbers, and sometimes, as range horses would join the mustangs, that would help keep the numbers up to about the same, for the range horses would soon get as wild as the mustangs themselves.

The long distances between water and feed didn't bother the wild horses near as much as it did the cattle. They was foaled on hard ground and their hoofs growed to be as hard as the sharp lava rock that covered it. They was near as light on their feet as the antelope that run on that same range and, like the antelope, they'd been crowded out of surrounding countries by wire fences of farms and ranches till they come to that land that was of mighty little use to man for his cattle, and of no use at all for sheep.

Of course that land of the mustang and antelope could be used for the better bred range horse, but the mustang would have to be got rid of first, like has been done in many such places, and so the range horses wouldn't lose their breeding by mixing with the wild ones. The range horse runs as free on the range as the mustang does, only he's used to seeing a rider more often, he won't try very hard to get away, and will turn as the rider wishes or to where he points him, and on into a corral without causing much trouble. In the corral the un-broke range horse is near as wild as the mustang. When first caught he'll fight just as much, and when first rode he'll usually buck harder and longer than the mustang will.

The average range horse originates from the mustang, only he's been bred up as to size for different purposes with imported thoroughbreds and to where he's worth raising and branding. The brand identifies the horse as to who he belongs to, and there's still many branded range horses who show some of the old time mustang blood.

The wild horse goes unbranded, of course. He's just as hard to round up and corral as antelope or deer would be, and if a rider crowds a wild bunch to go to a certain place, that wild bunch will scatter all directions, like a bunch of quail. A strong, hidden corral has to be built to catch them, that's called a blind trap. A water trap is a corral in plain sight and around a spring, one wide gate is sprung on 'em. They'll usually travel a long ways to some other watering place rather than go inside a water trap to drink, for the wild horse is mighty wise, and suspicious of any enclosure.

There's usually no claim on the wild horse, and any man who catches one has got himself a horse free, but there's the catch.

From what's been handed down to me from old-time cowboys who had the same handed down to them from other old-timers before them, and so on, back to the time when the first horses came to America, I get it that them horses was

Arabians, and a Spaniard by the name of Cortez brought 'em over by boat from Spain and landed 'em in Old Mexico, where they accumulated and some of 'em got away, run wild and drifted North. Them Arabian horses is the ones our mustangs originated from. They was a wild and sort of inbred bunch but they saved many a man and Indian from walking.

What we call mustangs now days has very little of that old mustang breed. That's been mostly bred out of 'em by imported horses, and them that's now running wild are just mixed breeds of range horses that didn't get rounded up regular, and hit for wild country where they seldom see a rider. Like in that wild horse desert country I was headed for. I was two days' ride away from the outfit, where I'd finished up on my job of breaking horses, when I come to a fair-sized cow town. I stayed there a couple of days, got all cleaned up, hair cut and trimmings, supplied up on a pack horse load of grub, clothes and all such as I needed, celebrated a bit and then hit out of town early one morning, headed on for the wild horse country. I had six good horses with me. There was only two I hadn't broke to ride as yet but I used 'em to pack, my grub supply was well tied down on one and the other hadn't been able to buck his pack off either. He was packing my bedding, extra clothes and warbag.

I was hazing my horses through a lane that led out of town a ways when I noticed two fresh horse tracks along the road, looked like only a couple of hours old on account I could see they was made after the night's dew fall had settled the dust. The fresh stirred earth made by their tracks stood out plain. One of the horse's tracks was of a fair-sized saddle horse, I figured. He was shod. The other horse's track was of a smaller horse and barefooted.

I didn't pay much attention to the two fresh horses' tracks only to glance at 'em, as a feller naturally will. That's a kind of range rider's instinct, to notice all signs and tracks, for stock will stray and the information of such tracks to some owner who might be hunting for them would be helpful to him, sometimes helpful in many other ways. A feller can never tell.

Them horse tracks stayed on the road ahead of me for many miles after leaving the lane that led out of town. I thought at first that the shod horse was being rode, on account of his tracks keeping so straight ahead, but later I seen where he'd sort of checked up to nip at some grass. Then I knowed he was a loose horse, and not wasting much time on his way to wherever him and the barefooted one was headed.

A few miles further on, the tracks branched off the road on a trail that led to some rough hills. I kept my horses on the road which seemed to circle around them same rough hills and sort of forgot about the fresh tracks. But I would have remembered seeing them tracks if any rider had asked me about 'em.

And I did remember them well, for, quite a few days afterwards and about a hundred and fifty miles from where I'd first seen 'em, I run into them very same tracks again and I recognized 'em quick. This time the tracks interested me a heap more. Them two horses sure must be travelling, I thought, for I hadn't wasted no time myself, and they sure must know of one certain range they was hitting for and anxious to get there because, on their trail, they'd had to go through a couple of pretty thickly settled valleys and skirt around or go through one or two towns. Then there was a wide river they had to swim acrost. There was no bridge that I know of to within a hundred miles either way and I crossed my horses on a ferry.

Well, thinking of what places they went through to get to where they wanted to get sure set me to wonder at them two horses, and their tracks got to be more than interesting to me.

But if I wondered about them then, I got to wondering about 'em plenty more as I drifted on, for their tracks seemed

tc be leading right the way I was headed, towards the wild horse territory. From the time I run into their tracks again this second time I run into them some more as I rode on. They was hitting pretty well straight acrost country and taking short cuts on and off trails, where, with me, I'd stick to easier going and sort of circle around the roughest parts. I know that in their cross-country drifting they crossed rimrocked and box canyons where it'd bother a mountain goat to climb in and out of, and as days went on and I run into their tracks now and again I then got to hankering to catch with 'em. I could see by their tracks and signs that they was seldom very far ahead of me, and sometimes I expected to see them after topping some ridge or mountain pass. I wondered how come they drifted so straight and steady. They seemed to graze and water as they went, seldom stopping, and as they come to bunches of horses, as they did many times, the shod track showed where they didn't stop to mix in and graze a while, as most horses would, but went right on as though they was mighty anxious to get to wherever they was going.

One morning I was camped by the first railroad track I'd seen since leaving the cow town about two hundred and fifty miles to the North. The railroad crossed a river there, and on account of high and solid rimrocks on both sides of the river, there was no way to get down and swim acrost or to get out on the other side. The only way to cross the river right at that place was on the railroad trestle and I sure wasn't going to take no chance of shoving my horses over that, they might get excited and jump in the river below or stick a leg and break it between the timbers of the trestle which was about three or four inches apart and allowed enough space for a hoof to go through.

There was only one way for me to go, that was either up or down the river till I come to a crossing or ferry or wagon bridge, and the going, either up or down that river looked plenty rough.

It was as I was sizing up the hills over my camp fire and by the sun's first rays that I got my first glimpse of the two horses that'd been making tracks ahead of me since I left the cow town. One was a bald-faced, stocking-legged black and the other was a bay filly. They both was good looking horses, specially while I was watching 'em, for they seemed excited as to finding a place to cross the river. They acted like they'd already been up and down it a few times looking for such a place, and when they come down off the hill and to the railroad they stopped, sniffed at the rails and then looked along the trestle, as if they would cross on that.

I was glad that my camp and horses was out of their sight because that might of scared 'em into crossing on the trestle. They trotted on down along the rim of the river and I figured they would find a place to cross down that way. But I'd just about got my outfit ready to pack, put out my fire and was going after my hobbled horses when I seen the two coming back, still on a trot and looking for a place to cross. They come to the railroad, stopped there and sized up the trestle again, more careful this time as if they figured that on the trestle was their only way to cross the river.

They didn't trot away from the trestle this time, they'd just wander a few yards and then come back to it. I watched 'em, feeling a little numb, because I knowed by their actions that they would try to cross that scary trestle.

They came to it once more, the black was in the lead, he lowered his head, snorted at the rails and timbers and made the first few steps on the start across. The filly was close by him.

I've witnessed some happenings that caused me to hold my breath but never any for so long a time as while watching them two horses crossing on that high and narrow trestle. I felt chilled and petrified and I don't think I could of moved if I wanted to or kept from watching the two horses. With heads low, bodies crouched and quivering, they snorted as they carefully made every step. One step gone wrong and there'd be a broken leg, or maybe two in the struggle to get free, and then maybe a fall into the swift river a hundred feet below.

As I watched I wished I had scared them away before they started acrost that trestle, but it was too late now. They went on, careful with every step, and as they got near the center of the trestle I was afraid they'd get scared at the height, the noise of the river below, the distance they still had to go, and turn to stampede back. That would of been their finish, either by broken legs or falling over the edge. And what if a train come along?

I think I'd given one of my horses right then just to see them two safe acrost the trestle and on solid earth on the other side. But as long as it seemed, it wasn't so very long when they got on the other side, then they let out a loud whistling snort at the spooky trestle they'd just crossed and hightailed it as fast as they could out of sight.

I rode up the river for a couple of days before I found a place to cross it, and as I rode I often wondered at the power of instinct to call free horses to cross such as the trestle which both was in dead fear of and which no amount of riders could of forced 'em to cross. It was the homing instinct of the wild horse that had called 'em, and I got proof of that some time later.

I'd got to the wild horse country I'd headed for. I'd found most of the scattered springs there had old dilapidated corrals around 'em, water traps. The wild horses had lost their suspicion of 'em and come right inside to water, and figuring on catching a few of them I located a little scope of country, high up where stock wouldn't naturally go and where feed was fairly good for my horses, and there I set up camp, about two miles from the closest spring, and went to work patching up the old corral at that spring so it would hold a bunch of wild ones when I sprung the gate on 'em. It wasn't a regular trap gate, just a swinging gate, but I fixed it so it would swing well, tied a long rope to it so that when pulled it would close the gate fast and tight. I dug me a pit as far as the long rope would reach, covered it up with brush and dirt, leaving only a hole big enough for me to crawl in and out, and I was ready for the wild ones to come.

But I didn't want to use that trap yet. I moved camp to another spring about thirty miles away and fixed another old trap there the same as I did the first, then I came back to the first trap and by that time the signs I'd made in fixing it had been pretty well blown over, and I noticed by tracks that quite a few bunches had come to water there.

My camp set up again, I went to the trap about sundown and got settled in my pit for the night, but no horses came that night nor the next, but the third night was good, a bunch came in. I counted eight head against the skyline and I pulled the gate slambang on the last one's tail as he went in.

The corral held 'em, and the next day I roped and throwed every one of 'em, tied a front foot to the tail with just enough rope so the foot only touched the ground and was useless for for any fast travelling. All the wild ones fixed up that way I went and got my saddle horses, packed up my outfit and brought all down to turn in with the wild ones, and then opened the corral gate and started out.

Being alone I had to do some tall riding to keep all the horses together but the wild ones couldn't get away with a front foot being held back, and when about four or five miles from the trap, they finally settled down to follow my saddle horses.

On account of the mustangs having one foot tied up I

could only drive 'em about fifteen miles the first day. There was no water in that distance and the horses was thirsty, so I changed saddle horses and rode all night as I let the horses graze and drift on slow. It was high noon the next day when I come to a spring and there I cooked myself a bait and let

the horses rest close to water the whole afternoon. When night come and it got cooler I started 'em on the move again, found water late the next day and in a corral close by I took the foot ropes off the mustangs. They was well "herd-broke" by then. That is, they would turn the way I wanted 'em and stay in one bunch, with my saddle horses.

I'd drove the horses about six days from the time I left the trap when I come to a big settled valley. In a lane leading to the town I met a rider who helped me drive the horses to the shipping yards on the outskirts of the town, and I sold 'em there the next day for eight dollars a head, a fair price for mustangs in that country.

My saddle horses rested up some, I headed back to the wild horse country. I used the second trap this time. Mustangs get suspicious quick if one trap is used often. I caught only a small bunch, six head, but being I had no way of keeping 'em till I caught another bunch, I took 'em in. They was all grown stuff and brought me ten dollars a head.

I think I caught and took in three more bunches after that. I remember there was fourteen head in one of the bunches I took in.

Fall was coming on, but the wild horse country was still hot and dry and I wanted to catch another bunch before a rain come, leaving plenty of water everwhere and making my traps useless.

I was at one of my traps early one evening. The sun hadn't gone down yet and I was enjoying a smoke by the shade of the corral when I seen two wild ones coming. I could tell they was thirsty because they was coming on a trot. I didn't want to bother with catching only two, but I didn't want to keep them from drinking, and I crawled into my pit without first investigating if rattlers or tarantulers had crawled in there, as they sometimes would.

The horses, always suspicious of a water trap, even if it hasn't been used for years, slowed up when they come within a few hundred yards of it and snorted and sniffed as they carefully came closer. It was then that I recognized the two horses. They was the two that had trailed ahead of me for over four hundred miles from the North. They was now on their home range and the reason I hadn't seen 'em before is that they'd been watering at other places in the wild horse country.

As I said before, I didn't want to bother with catching only two horses, and when them two came in the trap, and after they'd drank some, I somehow couldn't help but slam the gate closed on 'em. They was surprised, of course, as the gate slammed and they tore around some, but they soon quieted down again, and with a sort of hopeless look came to a standstill. They'd been caught before and they seemed to realize mighty well that their freedom was lost once again.

I got out of the pit and climbed into the corral. They only stood and quivered and snorted, and as I watched 'em I noticed that the black horse had wore his shoes off, but he had a little spot on his back that would never wear off, that was a saddle mark.

As usual when inside the trap I had my rope in my hand, and to get better acquainted with the black horse I made a loop and flipped it over his head. As I'd already figured long before, he was a broke horse and he didn't try to break away when I caught him. Instead he turned and faced me and only snorted a little as I pulled on the rope and led him up to me. He was gentle and whoever had broke him had not not broke his spirit. He was still the wild horse at heart, and if free again in his home range he now was in, he'd be harder to catch than the other wild ones which had never been caught. He'd be wiser and harder to get into traps. It was nothing against his wisdom that he'd been caught in my trap because it was old and sure looked desolated.

The black was far better built than the average wild horse in that country. He was good size too, and I judged him to be only about six years old. A good horse, and I figured I could sell him for near as much as I could get for any ten head of average wild ones I could catch there. The filly was good too, but fillies don't count much in the wild horse country.

I decided to keep the two horses. I went to where I'd hid

my saddled horse in the brush and rode to my camp where I crawled into my regular bed. Night had come but I didn't go to sleep for a long time, I got to thinking of the two horses in the trap, and as I did it came to me how much their freedom and home range meant to them. They'd run away from a country of plenty grass, shade and water, where they'd been well taken care of. Their condition proved that. Then they'd drifted acrost rough countries, through lanes and settlements every wild horse fears, swam rivers and even crossed on that scary trestle, all to get back to a desert and barren dry country. But that was their range, and wild freedom was there.

I thought again and again of their crossing that strange and spooky railroad trestle to get to that home range of theirs, and now, after only a short while of freedom they was in a trap again, and I'd closed the gate on 'em. I'd took away the freedom they'd risked so much to get back to.

The stars blinked down at me. I set up and rolled me a smoke and, still thinking of the two horses in the trap, it struck me kind of queer when it come to me of a sudden that there was nothing to stop me from opening that trap gate and giving the horses their freedom again. That thought seemed to relieve me a considerable. I finished my cigarette and then went right to sleep, all peaceful.

Who'd ever heard of wild horse hunter turning horses loose after he'd caught 'em? Such a thing is never thought of. As I rode down to the trap I got to thinking as I did the night before that a couple of horses more or less sure wouldn't make much difference to me, and whatever money they'd bring wouldn't mean so much either, not near as much as the pleasure of seeing them go free.

Besides, I had plenty enough money. I didn't need no new saddle and the rest of my outfit was good for plenty more wear, then I had a string of mighty good saddle horses and there was thousands of miles of range country. What more could a cowboy want?

But I was kind of cheated in the pleasure of carrying out my plans, for as I got to the trap I seen it was empty. Them two daggone horses had found a hole in the trap, they'd made it bigger and squeezed through.

Well, I thought, it was good thing they got away because I might of changed my mind. I looked down the big desert flat and couldn't even see their dust nowhere. I grinned as I thought how wise they was and how hard they'd be to trap again.

I patched the hole in the trap, figuring on catching one more bunch of wild ones before leaving that country. For I was again hankering for new range. I stayed in the pit two nights. No horses came, then big clouds piled up fast during the third afternoon, seemed like from nowhere, and I hardly felt the first few raindrops when whole sheets of it came, soaking me through.

It seldom rained in that desert, but when it did that time it didn't come down by drops but more by bucketfuls. In a short time every little dry wash was a roaring river, boulders was washed away like grains of sand, and from the high knoll I'd rode up onto I seen my trap washed away like it was made of toothpicks.

The cloudburst didn't last long, only about an hour, but it had sure moved a lot of country in that time. It was like big dams had broke loose from everywhere at once, and the big hardpan flats which was sizzling hot a few hours before was now transformed into big lakes. Plenty of water for the wild ones now, I thought, and they wouldn't be coming to water traps to drink for some weeks. By then more rain would most likely come, for winter wasn't far away.

The country sure looked clean and fresh and smelled good as the sun came up the next morning. It gave me the good feeling to ramble on over it, and as I boiled my coffee I got to thinking of another country I'd heard tell of and which I'd never seen. It was located some few hundred miles further on south, and as winter was coming on I figured the mild climate wouldn't go bad, for a spell anyway.

FIFTEENTH STORY

ONCE A COWBOY

I T WAS A mean fall, and on that account the round-up wagons was late with the works, and later getting in at the winter quarters. The cold raw winds of the early mornings wasn't at all agreeable to get up in, and I'd just about got so I could choke the cook when he hollered "Come and get it, you rannies, before I throw it out." We'd hear that holler long before daybreak, and sticking our heads out from under our tarps we'd greet the new day with a cuss word and a snort.

A wet snow would be falling and laying heavy on our beds, and feeling around between the tarp and blankets for socks we'd took off wet the night before, we'd find 'em froze stiff, but by the time they was pulled on and made to fit again and the boots over 'em, buckled on chaps and all what we could find to keep a feller warm, we wasn't holding no grudge against the cook, we just wanted a lot of that strong steaming hot coffee he'd just made and had waiting for us.

The bunch of us would amble up and around the fire like a pack of wolves, only there was no growling done; instead there'd be remarks passed around such as, "This is what makes a cowboy wonder what he done with his summer's wages." There'd be a whoop and a holler and a bucking cowhand would clatter up near top of the pots by the fire, "Make room, you waddies, Ise frizzed from my brisket both ways," and slapping his hands to his sides would edge in on the circle and grin at the bunch there before him.

The lids of the big dutch ovens was lifted, steaks, spuds and biscuits begin to disappear, but tracks was made most often toward the big coffeepot, and when the bait is washed down and the blood begins to circulate freer there was signs of daybreak, and rolling a cigarette we'd head for the muddy rope corral.

Our ropes would be stiff as cables, and it was hard to make a good catch. The particular pony you'd be wanting would most generally stick his head in the ground like a ostrich, and mixed in with about two hundred head of his kind and all a milling around steady, he'd be mighty hard to find again in case you missed your first throw.

Daylight being yet far off at that time, there's no way to identify any of the ten or twelve horses in your string only by the outline of their heads against the sky or by the white there may be on their foreheads. You throwed your rope but you couldn't see it sail and you didn't know you'd caught your horse till you felt the rope tighten up, and sometimes when you'd led out the horse you'd caught and got close to him it'd be another horse—the one you'd throwed the rope at had heard it coming and ducked.

Turning that horse back in the corral, you'd make another loop and try to get another sight of the horse you wanted; when you did, and the rope settled on him this time and let him out—if he didn't have to be drug out by a saddle horse—

to your saddle, then's when the fun most generally did begin.

The snow and sleet and cold wind made the ponies, young or old, mighty sensitive to whatever touched 'em; they'd kick, and buck, and strike then, no matter how gentle some of 'em might of been when the nice weather was on. The cowboy, all bundled up on account of the cold, his feet wet and in the slippery mud the wet snow had made, finds it all a big drawback in handling himself when saddling and a flying hoof comes.

The shivering pony don't at all welcome the frozen and stiff saddle blanket, and it might have to be put on the second time; getting a short hold and hanging on to the hackamore rope the cowboy then picks up the saddle and eases it on that pony's back, and before that pony can buck it off, a reach is made for the cinch, the latigo put through the cinch ring and drawed up. If you work fast enough and know how, all that can be done, and you don't have to pick up your saddle and blanket out of the mud.

I've seen it on many a morning of that kind and you'd just about have your pony half in the humor of being good, when some roman-nosed lantern-jawed bronc would go to acting up, jerk away from a rider and try to kick him at the same time and go to bucking and a bawling, and with an empty saddle on his back, hackamore rope a dragging, would make a circle of the rope corral where all the boys would be saddling up.

The ponies led out and shivering under the cold saddle that put a hump in their backs would just be a waiting for such an excuse as that loose hunk of tornado to start 'em, and with a loud snort and a buck half of 'em would jerk away. The cowboy had no chance holding 'em, for nine times out of ten that loose bronc would stampede past between him and the horse he was trying to hold, the hackamore rope would hook on the saddle of that bronc and it'd be jerked out of his hands.

Those folks who've seen rodeos from the grand stand most likely remember the last event of each day's doings; it's the wild-horse race, and maybe it'll be recollected how the track gets tore up by them wild ponies and how if one horse jerks loose he'll most likely make a few others break away. At them rodeos there's two men handling each horse, where with the round-up wagon on the range each man handles his horse alone.

And just picture for yourself the same happenings as you seen in the wild-horse race at the rodeo, only just add on to the picture that it's not near daylight, that instead of good sunshine and dry dirt to step on there's mud or gumbo six inches deep with snow and slush on top, the cowboy's cold wet feet, heavy wet chaps and coat that ties him down—a black cloudy sky, and with the cold raw wind comes a wet stinging snow to blind him.

That gives you a kind of an idea of how things may be along with the round-up wagon certain times of the year. Montana and Wyoming are real popular for rough weather as I've just described, and you can look for it there most every spring till late and sometimes in the fall starting early. I've seen that kind of weather last for two weeks at the time, clear up for one day and it was good to last for two weeks more.

It was no country for a tenderfoot to go playing cowboy in, besides the ponies of them countries wouldn't allow him to. It took nothing short of a long lean cowboy raised in the cow country to ride in it, and even though he'd cuss the weather, the country, and everything in general, there was a feeling back of them cuss words that brought a loving grin for the whole and the same that he was cussing.

Getting back to where a cowboy was saddling his horse and the stampeding bronc started the rumpus, I'll make it more natural and tell of how one little horse of that kind and on them cold mornings can just set the whole remuda saddled ponies and all to stampeding and leave near all the cowboys afoot.

Yessir, I remember well one cold drizzly morning that same fall, the wind was blowing at sixty per, the saddle blanket and saddle had to be put on at the same time or it'd blow out of the country. My horse was saddled and ready to top off, and pulling my hat down as far as I could get it I proceeds to do that. I'm getting a handful of mane along with a short holt on my reins and am just easing up in the saddle. When I gets up about half ways I meets up with the shadow of another horse trying to climb up on the other side of my horse. Me being only about a thousand pounds lighter than that shadow I'm knocked out of the way pronto, my horse goes down on part of me and that shadow keeps on a going as though there'd been nothing in its road.

That seemed to start things, and the wind that was blowing plenty strong already got a heap stronger, and all at once.

There was a racket of tearing canvas down by the chuck wagon and soon enough the big white tarpaulin that was covering that wagon breaks loose, comes a skipping over the brush, and then sails right up and amongst the two hundred saddle horses in the rope corral.

Them ponies sure didn't wait to see how and where it was going to light, they just picked up and flew, taking rope corral and everything right with 'em. A couple of the boys that was already mounted had to go too or else quit the pony they was riding, and they didn't have time to do that.

My horse being down for just the second he was knocked

that way was up and gone, and I sure has to do some tall scrambling when the remuda broke out of the corral. I could near touch 'em as they went by and I'm drawing a long breath for the narrow escape I just had, when that same long breath is knocked out of me and I sails a ways, then lands in a heap. There must of been one horse I hadn't accounted for.

It's about daylight when I comes to enough to realize that I should pick myself up and get out of that brush I'd lit into. I'm gazing around kind of light-headed and wonders where everybody went, and finally, figgering that they'd be by the fire at the chuck wagon, makes my way that direction.

It's broad daylight by the time we hears the bells of the remuda coming back to the corral, some of the boys had put it up again while I was asleep in the brush, and the two riders what stampeded away when the remuda did was hazing the spooky ponies in again.

"Well, boys, we'll try it again," says the wagon boss as he dabs his rope on a big brown horse that was tearing around the corral.

Most of our ponies being already saddled it don't take us long to get lined out again. The boss is up on his horse, taking a silent count to see if any of his men are missing, while waiting for everybody to be on their horses and ready to follow him.

Our horses was all spooked up from that stampede, and when we started away from camp that morning it was a wild bunch for fair. I was trying to ease my pony into a lope without him breaking in two with me, and I just about had him out of the notion when there's a beller alongside of me, and I turns to see a bucking streak of horseflesh with a scratching cowboy atop of it headed straight my way.

It's a good thing I was ready to ride, 'cause my horse had

been aching to act up from the start, and that example headed our way more than agreed with his spirits at that time. He went from there and started to wipe up the earth, and every time he'd hit the ground he'd beller, "I'll get you!"

At first I was satisfied to just be able to keep my saddle under me, but come a time when as my blood started circulating and getting warmed up on the subject that my spirits also answered the call and agreed with the goings on; then's when I begins to reefing him, and my own special war whoop sure tallied up with the bellering of that active volcano under me.

A glance to one side, and I notice that I'm not the only one who's putting up a ride, the rain and snow mixed kept me from seeing very far, but I could see far enough to tell that at least half the riders was busy on the same engagement that drawed my attention just then; one of the ponies had took a dislike for the cook and, tearing up everything as he went, was chasing him over pots and pans and finally under the wagon. The cowboy on top of that bronc was near losing his seat for laughing; he'd never seen the cook move that fast before.

We're out of camp a couple of miles before the usual rumpus quiets down, and stringing out on a high lope we all heads for a high point we don't see but know of, and some ten miles away. From that point the boss scatters the riders, and in pairs we branch out to circle and comb the country on the way back, running all the stock we see to the cutting grounds.

I'm riding along, trying to look through the steady-falling drizzle snow for stock; it seemed to me that I was born and raised under a slicker, on a wet saddle, riding a kinky bronc, going through slush and snow, and facing cold winds. It struck me as a coon's age since I seen good old sunshine, and for the first time I begins to wonder if a cow-puncher ain't just a plain locoed critter for sticking along with the round-up wagons as he does; it's most all knocks, and starting from his pony's hoofs on up to the long sharp horns of the ornery critters he's handling, along with the varieties the universe hands him in weather—twelve to sixteen hours in the saddle, three to four changes of horses a day, covering from seventy-five to a hundred miles, then there's one to two hours night guard to break the only few hours left to get rest in.

We was moving camp for the last time that year, the next stop was the home ranch, and when we hooked up the cook's six-horse team and handed him the ribbons we all let out a war whoop that started the team that direction on a high lope. The cook wasn't holding 'em back any, and hitting it down a draw to the river bottoms the flying chuck wagon swayed out of sight.

Us riders was bringing in upwards of a thousand head of weaners and we didn't reach the big fields till late that day, when we finally got sight of the big cottonwoods near hiding the long log building of the home ranch; that, along with the high pole corrals, the sheds and stables, all looked mighty good to me again.

The stock turned loose, we all amble towards the corrals to unsaddle; I tries to lead my horse in the dry stable, but him being suspicious of anything with a roof on won't have it that way. "All right, little horse," I says to him, "if you're happier to be out like you've always been used to, I'm not going to try to spoil you," and pulling off my wet saddle I hangs it where it's dry for once. The pony trots off a ways, takes a good roll and, shaking himself afterwards, lets out a nicker and lopes out to join the remuda.

"Just like us punchers," I remarks, watching him; "don't know no better."

Over eight months had passed since I'd opened a door and set my feet on a wooden floor, and when I walks in the bunk house and at one end sees a big long table loaded down with hot victuals, and chairs to set on, I don't feel at all natural, but I'm mighty pleased at the change.

The ranch cook is packing in more platters, and watching him making tracks around the table, looking comfortable

and not at all worried of what it may be like outside, I'll be daggone if I didn't catch myself wishing I was in his warm moccasins.

The meal over with, I drags a bench over by one of the windows and, listening some to the boys what was going over the events that happened on the range that summer, I finds myself getting a lot of satisfaction from just a-setting there and looking out of the window; it was great to see bum weather and still feel warm and comfortable. I gets to stargazing and thinking, so that I plum forgets that there's twenty cowboys carrying on a lot of conversation in the same big room.

I'd just about come to the conclusion I was through punching cows when one of the boys digs me in the ribs and hollers, "Wake up, Bill! Time for second guard."

I did wake up, and them familiar words I'd heard every night for the last eight months struck me right where I lived; they was said as a joke, but right there and then I was sure I'd never want to stand no more of them midnight guards.

The work was over, and all but a few of the old hands was through. The superintendent gave us to understand as a parting word that any or all of us are welcome to stay at the ranch and make ourselves to home for the winter. "You can keep your private saddle horses in the barn and feed 'em hay. The cow foreman tells me," he goes on, "that you've all been mighty good cowboys, and I'm with him in hoping to see you all back with the outfit in time for the spring works."

A couple of days later finds me in town, my own top horse in the livery stable and me in a hotel. I makes a start to be anything but a cowboy by buying me a suit, a cap, shoes, and the whole outfit that goes with the town man. I then visits the barber and the bathtub, and in an hour I steps out thinking that outside my complexion and the way I walks I looks about the same as everybody else I see on the street.

I takes it easy for a few days, then gradually I tries to break myself to looking for a job where there's no ponies or bellering critters to contend with. I wanted an inside job where the howling blizzard wouldn't reach me and where I could have a roof over my head at night insted of a tarpaulin.

Time goes on, and it seems like my education is lacking considerable to qualify for the job I set out to get; you had to know as much as a schoolma'am to even get a look in. I made a circle every day and run in all the likely places I'd see.

I'm some leg weary as I makes my way back to the hotel one night, and going to my room I stretches out on the bed to rest up a little before I go out to eat. I have a feeling that all ain't well with me as I lays there thinking.

I don't want to think that I'm hankering to get back to the range, so blames it to the new ways of everything in general what comes with town life, and I tries to cheer myself up with the idea that I'll soon get used to it and in time like it.

"I got to like it," I says to myself, "and I'm going to stay with it till I do, 'cause I'm through with punching cows"; and getting up real determined I goes out to hunt a restaurant.

I'd been feeding up on ham and eggs and hamburger steak with onions ever since I hit town, and this night I thought I'd change my order to something more natural and what I'd been used to on the range.

"Bring me a rib steak about an inch thick," I says to the waiter. "Don't cook it too much, but just cripple the critter and drag 'er in."

I kept a waiting for the order to come, and about concluded he must of had to wait for the calf to grow some, when here he comes finally. I tackles the bait on the platter, and I was surprised to see a piece so much like beef, and still taste so different from any I'd ever et before. With a lot of work I managed to get away with half of it, and then my appetite, game as it was, had to leave me.

The waiter comes up smiling as he sees I'm about through, and hands me the bill. "I don't want to spread it around," I says as I picks up the bill and goes to leave, "but between you and me, I'll bet you that steak you brought me has been cooked in the same grease that's been cooking my ham and eggs these last two weeks. I can taste 'em."

The weather had been good and stayed clear ever since I hit town, but as I walks out of the restaurant I notice a breeze had sprung up, and snow was starting to fall. I finds myself taking long whiffs of air that was sure refreshing after stepping out of that grub-smelling emporium.

Feeling rested up some, I faces the breeze for a walk and to no place in particular. I'm walking along, thinking as I go, when looking around to get the lay of my whereabouts I notices that right across the street from where I'm standing is the livery stable where I'd left my horse, and being that I'd only been over to see him once since I'd rode in, thinks I'd enjoy the feel of his hide once more.

The stable man walks in on us as we're getting real sociable, and with a "Howdy" asks if I may be looking for a job. "Man named Whitney, got a ranch down the river about fifty miles, asked me to look out for a man who'd want a job breaking horses on contract, and I thought maybe you'd be wanting to take it."

"Not me," I says, feeling tempted and refusing before

considering. "I'm not riding any more, and I been looking
for work in town."

"Did you try the Hay and Grain Market next block up the
street?" he asks. "They was looking for a man some time
back."

No, I hadn't tried it, but the next day bright and early I
was on the grounds and looking for the major-domo of that
outfit.

At noon that day I'd changed my suit, and putting on a
suit of Mexican serge I went to work. My job was clerking,
and on the retail end of the business, filling in orders and
help load the stuff on the wagon of the customers.

And that night, when the place closed up and I walks to
my hotel I felt a heap better than any time since I'd hit
town. Of course I wasn't in love with the job, it was quite a
change and mighty tame compared to punching cows, but
then I figgered a feller had to allow some so's to get what
he's after.

I gets along fine with everybody around, and it ain't long
before I'm invited to different gatherings that's pulled off
now and again. I gets acquainted more as I stays on, and
comes a time when if feeling sort of lonesome I know where
to go and spend my evenings.

I'd manage to stop in at the stable and say "Hello" to my
gray horse most every night when the work was through, and
with everything in general going smooth I thought it wasn't
so bad.

There was times though when coming to my room I'd find
myself staring at my chaps and boots with the spurs still on
and where I'd put 'em in the corner. They got to drawing
my attention so that I had to hide 'em in the closet where I

couldn't see 'em, and then I thinks, "What about my horse and saddle? A town man don't have no need for anything like that."

But somehow I didn't want to think on that subject none at all right then, and I drops it, allowing that a feller can't break away from what all he's been raised with or at in too short a time.

That winter was a mean one, just as mean as the fall before, I still remembered; the snow was piled up heavy on the hills around town and every once in a while there'd be another storm adding on a few inches. The sight of it and the cold winds a howling by on the streets kept me contented some, and it all helped break me in to the new ways of living I'd picked on.

I'd been on the job a month or so when I notice that my appetite begins to leave me. I changes eating places often, but they all seemed to have the same smell as you walked in, and there was times when I felt like taking the decorated platter and all outside and eating it there.

And what's more, my complexion was getting light, too light.

*   *   *   *   *

January and February had come and went, the cold spell broke up some, and then March set in wild and wicked. I'm still at my job at the Feed Market and my wages being raised once along with promises of another raise soon, proves that I'm doing well. What's more, my time had been took up considerable on account of me meeting up with a young lady what put my gray horse a far second in my thoughts, and when I'd walk past the stable I'd most generally be in too big a hurry to stop and see him. One day the stable man stops me as I'm hurrying by and tells me that he has a chance to sell that little horse for me for a hundred dollars.

That was a call for a show-down to myself, and of a sudden I realized that parting with that horse I was parting with the big open range I'd been born and raised into. I studies it over for quite a spell and finds the more I thinks the more my heart lays the ways of where that horse can take me, and my mind all a milling I can't decide.

I walks away, telling the stable man I'd let him know later.

I does a lot of comparing between the range and the town, and finds that both has qualities and drawbacks, only in town it was easier living, maybe too easy, but I figgered that here was more of a future.

Just the other day I was told by the main owner at the market that they was figgering on quitting the business and retiring, and that there'd be a good opportunity for a serious-thinking man like myself to grab. It was suggested that I could let my wages ride and buy shares with 'em as I worked till there'd come a time as I kept at it when I'd find myself part owner of a good business and a steady income.

That night I went to see the young lady, who by this time had a lot to say as to my actions. I didn't let her know what was going on in my think tank, 'cause I wanted to fight it out by myself; besides I'd come to conclusions, and long before I left her to go back to my hotel.

The next morning I stops by and tells the stable man that if he can get a hundred dollars for that little horse of mine, to take it. But it hit me pretty hard and I didn't go by the stable any more after that, not for a long time.

April come, and with the warm weather that came with it the snow started to melting, the streets was muddy, and the gutters was running full; it was spring, and even with all the resolutions I'd made, I didn't feel any too strong right then.

I was afraid to give my imagination full swing and think of the home ranch on the Big Dry; I knew the boys that came back for the spring works would be out on the horse round-up and getting ready to pull out with the wagons.

Each cowboy would be topping off his string about now, the bronc peeler would be picking out a bunch of green colts from the stock horses and start in breaking, the cook would be a cleaning up the chuck box on the back end of that wagon, and the cow foreman, glancing often on the road that leads from town to the ranch, would be looking for any of the missing cowboys what was with him the year before.

I found it mighty hard to walk away from that spring sunshine into the building where I was working. There was orders on the desk waiting for me to fill, and picking 'em up I walks among high walls of grain and baled hay.

Everybody I'd see would remark how great it was outside in the spring air, and rubbing their hands would get to work at the desk and typewriter, and forget all about it the minute they set down.

I felt sorry for 'em in a way, 'cause it struck me as though they'd never had a chance to really appreciate springtime—or was it that their years in captivity that way had learnt 'em better than to hanker for such?

Anyway, I sure didn't seem to be able to dodge how I felt. My girl and everybody else noticed it, and even though I'd try to laugh it off I'd soon find myself picturing little white-faced calves scattered out either playing or sunning themselves while their mammies was feeding on the new green grass.

I could near feel the slick shiny hide of the ponies after their long winter hair had just fell off. And dag-gone it, it was getting the best of me.

I'd catch myself sneaking glances at the green hills around the town and feeling as though I had no right to. And once in a while in the evening as I'd be walking to my room and I'd hear a meadow lark a-singing way off in the distance, I'd look at the buildings, the sidewalks and streets as though they was a scab on this earth. I wanted my horse under me and lope out away from it.

I'd done a heap of reasoning with myself, and kept a pointing out all the whys I should forget the range and get used to the town, and I'd pretty near give in as long as I was in my room and couldn't feel the breeze, but once outside again and a meadow lark sang out, my heart would choke out all what the town offered and leave breath only for the blue ridges and the big stretches that layed past 'em.

Then came a day when my hide got too thick to feel the reasoning spur I was giving it. Something way deep inside of me took charge of things and I finds myself making tracks towards the stable.

I sneaks in, and I had to rub my eyes considerable to make sure that there in the same box stall was my little gray horse, fat as a seal and a snorting like a steam engine.

"Dag-gone your hide!" I says, and I makes a grab for him, he's pawing the air snorting and a rearing, but I'm hanging on to his neck with a death grip and hands him all the pet cuss words I can think of.

The stable man runs up to see what's making all the rumpus, and his expressions tell me plain he thinks I'm drunk and celebrating. I was drunk all right, but not on the same stuff that's handed over the bar.

"Sorry I couldn't sell him for you," I hear him say as I let go of my horse and walks up to him, "but the fellow what wanted him came over one day to try the horse out and the little son of a gun throwed him off as fast as he'd get on; he brought another feller over the next day and the same thing happened. Too bad he acts that way," he goes on, "'cause he's a right pretty horse."

"You're dag-gone right he's a pretty horse," I says; "the prettiest horse I ever seen."

It's three days later when I gets sight of the Triangle F main herd, then the remuda, and down in a creek bottom by a bunch of willows is the chuck wagon.

There's war whoops from the bunch as I lopes into sight, and the wagon boss comes up to meet me. "I knowed you'd be back, Bill," he says, smiling, "and I got your string of ponies a waiting for you, twelve of 'em."

And on guard that night, riding around the bedded herd, I was singing a song of the trail herd, happy again, and just a cowboy.